Directions: Print the capital letters of the alphabet. Print the small letters of the alphabet.

Can you print the ABC's?

Aa

AaBbCc

Directions: In the top 4 rows print the letter that comes between the given letters. In the bottom 4 rows print the letters that come before and after the given letters.

m ___ o	t ___ v	d ___ f
a ___ c	p ___ r	l ___ n
g ___ i	b ___ d	r ___ t
o ___ q	j ___ l	u ___ w
___ k ___	___ w ___	___ e ___
___ s ___	___ o ___	___ q ___
___ d ___	___ h ___	___ v ___
___ m ___	___ x ___	___ c ___

Directions: Begin at ★, and follow the alphabet from dot to dot to form a letter. Find the letter, capital and small, in the words at the right. Draw a ring around the letter each time you find it.

a★ b e f c• •d j• •i i k h g	Happy hello birthday surprise Here Mother	d★ e g h f m• •k i o n j i
something make rain Some Must Name		
m★ n •o p r q	look Little Hello milk Sally will	p★ q s t w• •r y x v u
Nuts know children farm new soon		
s★ t z y v u x w	Wants letters help Tom went Time	u★ v x y •w z
Live loves Vine every went ever		

3

LESSON 2: TEST: ALPHABETICAL SEQUENCE

Directions: Print the missing letters. At the bottom print the missing letters of the alphabet.

c	h	j	k	e
k	n	p	i	b
d	c	e	c	g
q	r	t	w	m
n	p	r	y	x
p	s	u	r	o
y	d	f	v	s
s	b	d	z	n

a	f	k	m
n	q	u	z

4

Directions: Say the name of the picture. Print the capital and small letters for the beginning sound. Color the pictures.

Directions: Say the name of the picture. Print the letter for the beginning sound. Color the pictures.

___ie	___ig	___un	___all
___in	___ap	___ire	___ive
___am	___et	___ug	___og

Directions: Say the name of the picture. Print the letter for the ending sound.
Color the pictures.

to____   we____   do____   be____

pai____   cu____   su____   bu____

ha____   lea____   bo____   dru____

Directions: Say the name of the picture. Print the small letter for the ending sound. Color the pictures.

Directions: Say the name of the picture. Draw a red ring around the letter for the beginning sound. Draw a blue ring around the letter for the ending sound.

d r p l	v t b f	d b m p
c t d q	a x s g	p g b d
b p j g	l f g h	h r s t
q n w v	v n r h	t l b k

Directions: Say the name of the picture. If you hear the consonant at the beginning, draw a ring around the consonant at the left. If you hear it at the end, draw a ring around the one at the right.

Directions: Say the name of the picture. Print the letter for the beginning sound. Then print the letter for the ending sound to complete the name for each picture.

e	o	u
o	a	i
e	u	o
i	a	e

11

Directions: Say the name of the picture. Print the letter for the sound you hear in the middle of the word. The first one shows you what to do.

d

Directions: Say the name of the picture. Print the middle letter in the space to complete its name.

dra on

le on

ra io

ca in

ti er

pea ut

spi er

ca el

Ted will get his wa_____on.

I can see se _____ en bugs.

Color the wa_____on red.

Color the se _____ en bugs green.

Jill has six coo_____ies.

See the tu _____ ip in the vase.

Color the coo_____ies brown.

Color the tu _____ ip yellow.

13

Directions: Say the name of the picture. In the spaces below each picture, print the letters for the beginning, middle, and ending sounds.

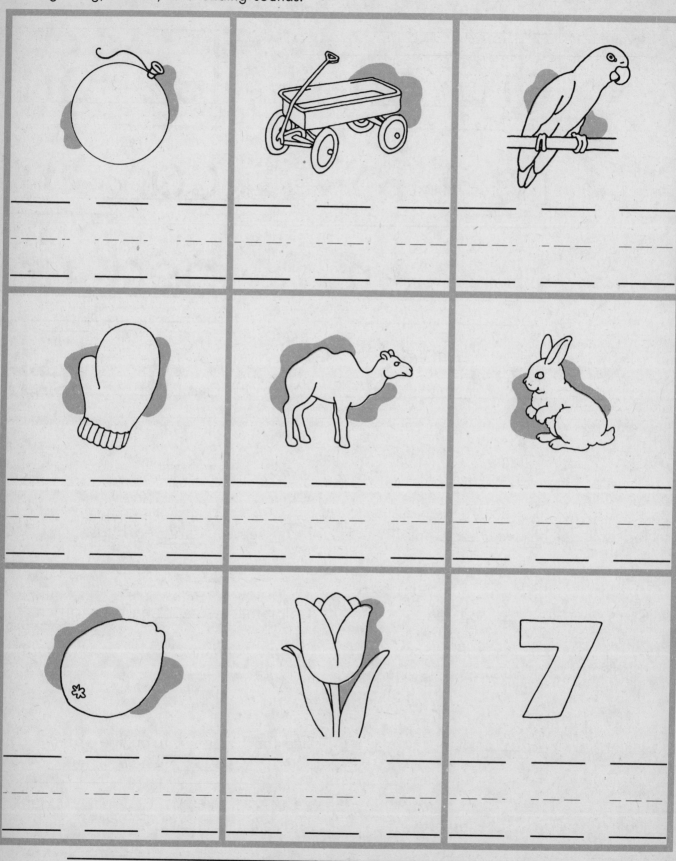

Directions: Draw a ring around the name of the picture. Color all the pictures.
 If a word or syllable has only one vowel and it comes at the beginning or between two consonants, the vowel usually stands for a short sound.

hat ham	bag hat	camp lad
hand had	bat bad	lap lamp
sad back	cat cap	tam jam
bag bat	cab can	Jan Sam
wax ax	mat man	tag tan
am at	fan tan	tap tack
and an	cat can	mad man
at ant	cab cap	map mat

15

Directions: Read the list of words. Draw a ring around the word that does not rhyme. Draw its picture. Read the words to your teacher.

cat		Max		cap	
fan		tax		tap	
hat		bag		map	
mat		wax		cab	
sack		bag		sand	
hand		rag		land	
back		cap		pan	
tack		tag		band	
ham		sad		quack	
fan		bat		cat	
ran		bad		sack	
can		had		back	
hand		pan		sat	
land		fan		ax	
lamp		Dan		pat	
sand		hat		fat	

Directions: Say the name of the picture, and print its name below. Then print a word that rhymes with it. Do what the sentences tell you to do.

Color the bag red.

Color the fan green.

Color the cap red.

Color the hat blue.

Color the cat black.

Color the tack yellow.

Color the lamp green and black.

Color the pan red and yellow.

LESSON 9: RECOGNIZING SHORT A

Directions: Draw a ring around the word that will complete each sentence, and print it on the line. Read the sentence to be sure that it makes sense.

_____

1. A _____ at bat had a cap.   band   man   sack

2. Ann had a pal at the _____ .   cat   lamp   camp

3. Pam has a tan _____ .   ran   van   jam

4. Hand the bag of _____ to the man.   sand   hand   band

5. An _____ ran past the sack.   ant   an   at

6. _____ the jam and ham to Nat.   Must   Bass   Pass

7. Jan had a can of _____ .   rap   has   gas

8. Dan swam back to _____ .   land   band   fast

9. At _____ I ran as fast as Mac.   sat   last   tack

10. Val and Pat _____ bags at camp.   pan   back   pack

Directions: Draw a ring around the name of the picture. Color all the pictures.
If a word or syllable has only one vowel and it comes at the beginning or between two consonants, the vowel usually stands for a short sound.

silk milk mill bill	mitt bit fit mill	lid hid lip tip
tips lips dips dill	big pig fig pit	Bit Bib Bill Hill
Tin Fill Jill Jim	bill bit hit bib	ink wink sink pink
hill bill sill mitt	mix six fix bit	win tin will pin

Directions: Say the words in the ball. Color the parts of each ball that have rhyming words the same color.

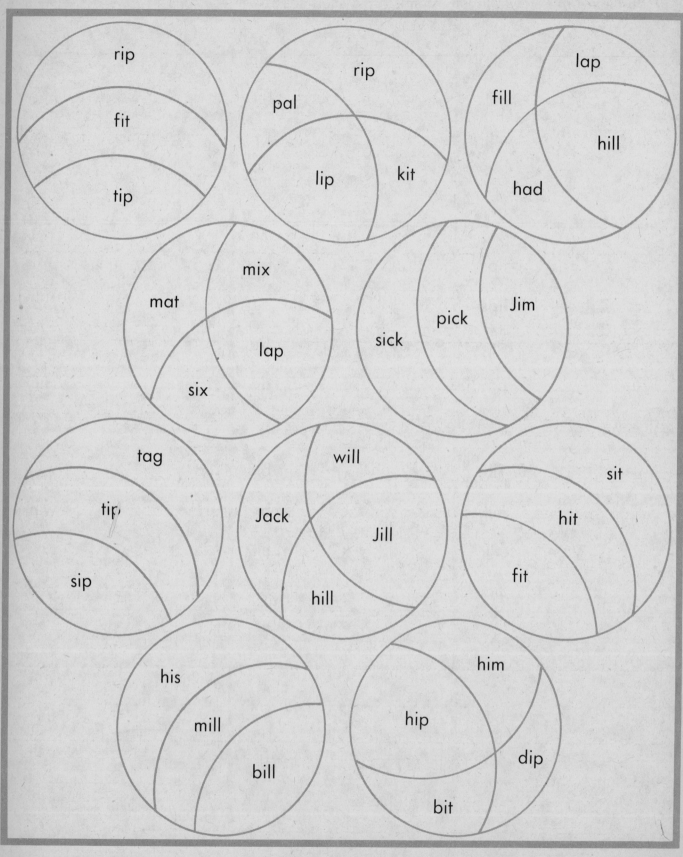

20

Directions: Say the name of the picture, and print its name below. Then print a word that rhymes with it. Color the pictures.

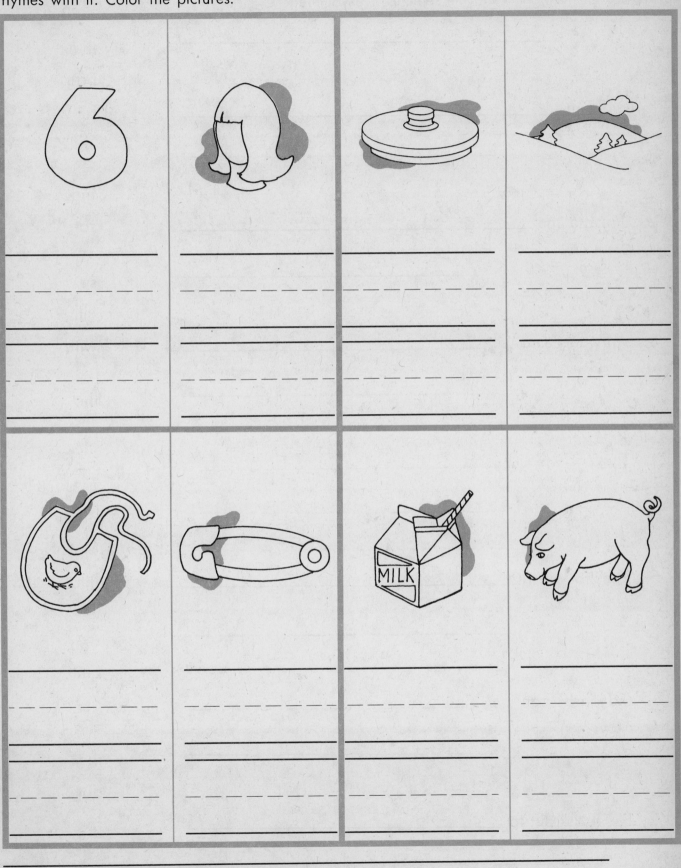

Directions: Read the words that are part of a sentence. Finish the sentence using all the words in the box at the right. Read the sentences to your teacher.

1. Did Tim _____ ?

the
bag
fill

2. Jim hid the _____ .

cat
big
fat

3. Ann and Kim will _____ .

sit
Bill
with

4. The cat will _____ .

the
rip
sack

5. The lid will fit _____ .

pan
big
the

6. Sid and I can _____ .

six
quit
at

7. I will ask Jill to _____ .

the
bat
fix

Directions: Draw a ring around the word that will complete each sentence, and print it on the line. Read the sentence to be sure that it makes sense.

1. Dan had a _____ for Rick.   him   gift   lift

2. A pan of milk is in the _____ .   sink   rink   sank

3. The cat hid in a _____ hat.   big   bag   bat

4. Ann will _____ the lamp.   band   mix   fix

5. Kim had a sip of _____ .   mile   milk   wick

6. I will dig and dig in the _____ .   mad   hand   sand

7. The man will sit on the _____ .   hill   fill   tan

8. Lin and Dad _____ in the cab.   sick   fat   sat

9. The tin pan had a big _____ .   limp   lid   ran

10. Nick's mitt will fit in the _____ .   hill   miss   bag

Directions: Draw a ring around the name of the picture. In the box print the letter that stands for the vowel sound you hear in the word.

If a word or syllable has only one vowel and it comes at the beginning or between two consonants, the vowel usually stands for a short sound.

cap cup	gas gull	Dick duck
kit	gum	Dad
can cup	jug jam	tug tip
cap	just	bug
but nuts	calf cut	sack six
nap	cuff	sick
ask ax	as bun	sun sum
is	bus	dim

Directions: Read the words in the box above the pictures, and find the picture that goes with each word. Then print the name of each picture in the space below it.

bud	cup	rug	bus	bug	sun
gum	pup	cuff	tub	jug	duck

25

Directions: Read each riddle. Find the correct answer in the word list, and print it on the line.

I am full of milk.	I can say, "Bow, wow."	You can eat me.
What am I?	What am I?	What am I?
_____	_____	_____
- - - - - - -	- - - - - - -	- - - - - - -
_____	_____	_____
up cut	cup up	cut but
cup cuff	pup cut	fun nut

I hid in the jug.	A hot dog fills me up.	We can do this.
What am I?	What am I?	What is it?
_____	_____	_____
- - - - - - -	- - - - - - -	- - - - - - -
_____	_____	_____
bus tub	dug bun	just lump
sun bug	fun run	muff jump

This is fun to do.	You can ride in me.	You can see me.
What is it?	What am I?	What am I?
_____	_____	_____
- - - - - - -	- - - - - - -	- - - - - - -
_____	_____	_____
fun run	bud bug	sun but
bun cup	bus us	run fun

I say, "Quack, Quack."	We do this to Dad.	A pig digs in this.
What am I?	What is it?	What is it?
_____	_____	_____
- - - - - - -	- - - - - - -	- - - - - - -
_____	_____	_____
tuck luck	up lump	just but
pup duck	sun hug	mud must

Directions: Draw a ring around the word that will complete each sentence, and print it on the line. Read the sentence to be sure that it makes sense.

_____ — — — — — — — 1. A duck cannot _____ fast.	rug run bat cup
_____ — — — — — — — 2. Ann's _____ can jump up to the tub.	pup bus cup rug
_____ — — — — — — — 3. We had a _____ full of milk.	but cut jug nuts
_____ — — — — — — — 4. Gus and Kim _____ in the mud.	cub bus rug dug
_____ — — — — — — — 5. Pam and I will sit in the _____ .	bun sun gum dug
_____ — — — — — — — 6. Did you see the yellow bug in the _____ ?	just lug dust must
_____ — — — — — — — 7. Russ and Judd run and _____ at camp.	jump mumps bump lump

Directions: Make new words by changing the vowels. Print the new words on the lines. The first one is started for you.

Can you help Jack?

Can you help Jill?

	i	u
fan	fin	
bad		
ham		
hat		
as		
bag		

Directions: Have fun with these questions. Draw a ring around the correct answer.

1. Can a black pup run with Max?	Yes	No
2. Is a big cup a little nut?	Yes	No
3. Is the sun black?	Yes	No
4. Can a cat run fast?	Yes	No
5. Can a big pig sing for you?	Yes	No
6. Can we nap in a tan van?	Yes	No
7. Can a man run up a hill?	Yes	No
8. Is a green rug red?	Yes	No
9. Is Ann a big map?	Yes	No
10. Can you sit on a bus?	Yes	No
11. Can a little cup run fast and jump?	Yes	No
12. Will a cat hug a rat?	Yes	No
13. Can you fill a pan with milk?	Yes	No
14. Can a doll jump on the bus?	Yes	No
15. Can a pig go as fast as a cab?	Yes	No
16. Can you rub your hands?	Yes	No
17. Is a sad cat happy?	Yes	No
18. Can a bus be big?	Yes	No
19. Can a bug sit in the mud?	Yes	No

Directions: Read the words in the box above the pictures, and find the picture that goes with each word. Then print the name of each picture in the space below it.

If a word or syllable has only one vowel and it comes at the beginning or between two consonants, the vowel usually stands for a short sound.					
top	mop	pot	box	Tom	sock
cot	doll	fox	lock	rock	rod

_____

_____

_____

_____

_____

_____

_____

_____

_____

_____

_____

_____

Directions: Draw a ring around the name of the picture. Color all the pictures.

fix cob fox six	pot top tap pit	bill sill dill doll
cot dot job cut	dug dog dig pot	rob rid rap rod
pig pop pup pat	lag log bug lot	luck lock lick lack

Directions: Draw a ring around the sentence that tells about the picture. Draw a box around each short **O** word in the sentences.

	The fox is not on the log. The fox is in the log. The fox is on the log. The fox is under the log.
	Bob lost his socks. Bob sat on a big rock. Bob is on top of the big log. Bob has a big rock in his hand.
	The dog ran to the box. The mop is not in the box. I will hop, hop, hop to the log. See the doll in the box.
	I got the doll on the cot. Jill can see the big top. The big top is on the mop. The red top is in Bob's hand.
	Hot milk is in a pot. The big doll is in the box. The milk in the cup is hot. The big red top is for Ron.

Directions: Draw a ring around the name of the picture.

six fix	bun hit	doll bill	tan fan
sit sun	box fox	dot dog	fun fin
cup cap	mat cot	sick sock	rock luck
kit can	mop pop	son sack	lock sock
fix fox	pin top	tick rack	pot dug
box fun	pot tip	tuck rock	dog log

Directions: Print the name of each picture in the space below it.

Directions: Draw a ring around the word in the list at the right that will complete each sentence. Then print the word on the line. Read the sentence to be sure that it makes sense.

1. Ron is fond of his pet _____ .   Jack

2. I see a bug with dots on _____ back.   bus

3. Jan will ride in the yellow _____ .   duck

4. Rick and _____ will fill the bag with nuts.   its

5. I will _____ up to the pond.   jog

---

1. Jim and Dan got a _____ tan.   full

2. Dot has a box _____ of pins.   rock

3. Mom can toss the ring into the _____ .   sun

4. Tom sat on a big _____ .   hot

5. I will sip the _____ milk.   box

Directions: Print the name of the picture on the line with the same numeral as the picture. Color the pictures.

If a word or syllable has only one vowel and it comes at the beginning or between two consonants, the vowel usually stands for a short sound.

1 _____

2 _____

3 _____

4 _____

5 _____

6 _____

7 _____

8 _____

9 _____

10 _____

Directions: First, read the sentences and do what they tell you to do. Then print the name of each picture on the line next to it.

1. Find the bed.

   Color it red and blue.

2. Find the hen.

   Color it yellow.

3. Find the nest.

   Color three eggs red
   and three eggs blue.

4. See the tent.

   Color it yellow.

5. See the belt.

   Color it green.

6. Find the vest.

   Color it red and black.

37

Directions: Draw a ring around the word that will complete each sentence, and print it on the line. Read the sentence to be sure that it makes sense.

1. Red Hen sat on the _____ . nest   best   bet

2. Can Ron mend his _____ ? pop   socks   tocks

3. Ken's blue jet _____ off the box. bet   fell   fill

4. Lin will run and _____ the bat. get   met   bad

5. Mom can see _____ hop and jump. us   is   as

6. I sat at Meg's _____ . dust   desk   dill

7. The _____ has blue ink in it. pen   pin   pill

8. Tell Ed to _____ Mom. held   vest   help

9. Jill has a _____ truck full of rocks. red   fed   led

10. He has a _____ and a cap in the box. bet   let   belt

Directions: In the top part, print the name of each picture. At the bottom, read each sentence. Then print **yes** or **no** on the line at the right.

1. You can nap in a bed.

2. I can get ten eggs for the box.

3. A cat has six legs.

4. A big bus can jump up and down.

5. Mom can help get a can of gas.

6. You can go fast in a jet.

7. An ant is as big as an ox.

39

Directions: Read each sentence that is started for you. Read the word at the right of the sentence. Change the vowel in the word to make a new word that will complete the sentence. Print the word on the line. The first one shows you what to do.

1. Bev left the quilt on the **bed** .   bad

2. Yes, the sun will _____ in the west.   sat

3. The vet will help the _____ .   pop

4. The cat _____ up the milk in the pan.   lips

5. Pat will help us _____ the rock.   left

1. Can Max lift the _____ box off the bus?   bag

2. Lock the box and set it on the _____ .   disk

3. Miss Nell _____ the pen on the desk.   lift

4. Did the dog run to Bob and _____ his hand?   lack

5. A gust of wind _____ the tent.   hat

Directions: In the top box, print the name of each picture. In the middle, change the vowel to make a new word. At the bottom, find the word for each sentence, and print it in the space.

tug _____   rip _____   tab _____

fox _____   fad _____   hunt _____

rust _____   sand _____   tint _____

1. Hand Judd his _____ and socks.   lit

2. Sam fell in the _____ and got wet.   belt

3. At dusk Mom _____ the lamp on the desk.   pond

Directions: In the top part, make two words out of each word you see. In the bottom part, the name of each picture has two syllables. Print the missing syllable in the space.

catfish		handcuffs	
sunset		windmill	
milkman		bathtub	
tiptop		uphill	

bon	_____	_____	ten
rab	_____	_____	py
kit	_____	_____	bon
dust	_____	_____	ket

Directions: Read each sentence. Find the missing word, and print it on the line.

If a one-part word or syllable has two vowels, the first vowel usually stands for a long sound, and the second is silent.

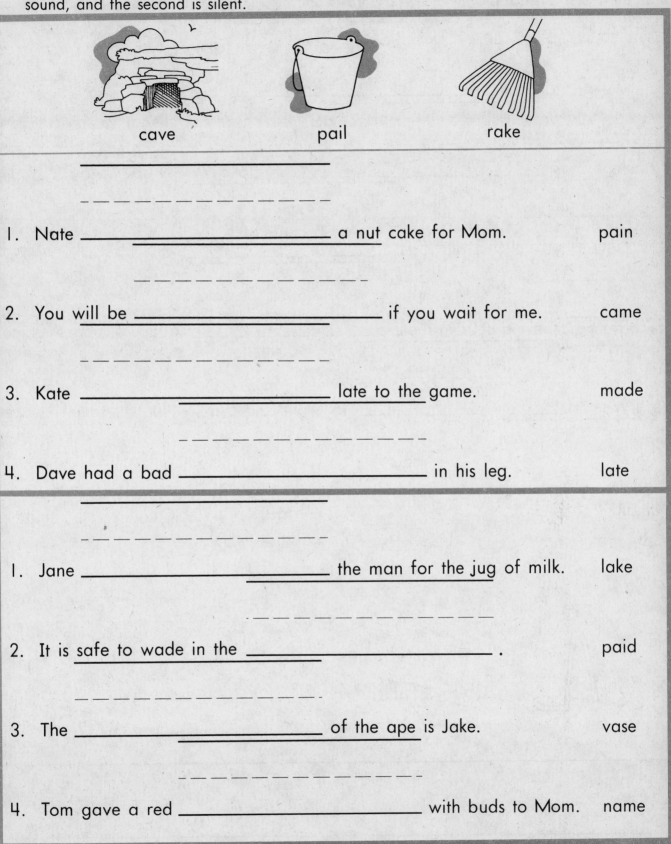

cave   pail   rake

1. Nate _____ a nut cake for Mom.   pain

2. You will be _____ if you wait for me.   came

3. Kate _____ late to the game.   made

4. Dave had a bad _____ in his leg.   late

1. Jane _____ the man for the jug of milk.   lake

2. It is safe to wade in the _____ .   paid

3. The _____ of the ape is Jake.   vase

4. Tom gave a red _____ with buds to Mom.   name

Directions: In the top part, draw a ring around the word that belongs in each sentence. Then print it on the line. In the middle part, draw a ring around each long **A** word. At the bottom, print the name of each picture. Use the words from the middle of the page.

1. We got tape at the _____ .   sap   sale   same

2. Jane may _____ in the lake.   wade   way   with

3. Dave gave Kay the big red _____ .   fat   fake   rake

4. Did you see the cubs in the _____ ?   cape   cave   came

5. Will you _____ to Mom and Dad?   sat   save   wave

| tap | tape | cap | cape | at | ate |
| mail | mat | rain | gate | hay | ham |

LESSON 21: RECOGNIZING LONG I

Directions: At the top, draw a ring around the name of each picture. At the bottom, find the word that belongs in each sentence, and print it on the line.

fin fire	pig pile	bike big	bib bite

I will pay a _____ for it.

dime   dim   dill

Jill will _____ the ball.

hate   hill   hit

He will ride his _____ .

big   bike   like

Mike sees a bee _____ .

fit   fine   hive

A bug has _____ legs.

sick   hide   six

Lil has a big red _____ .

kit   time   kite

Jane will bake a _____ .

pipe   pie   pill

I _____ to dive.

life   like   lick

45

Directions: In the top part, draw a ring around the word that belongs in each sentence. Then print it on the line. In the middle part, draw a ring around each long **I** word. At the bottom, print the name of each picture. Use the words from the middle of the page.

_____

1. Take your _____ to the lake.　　big　　bike　　bite

2. Mike will tie a tail to his _____ .　　kite　　kit　　hide

3. Kim likes to _____ the bus.　　hid　　rid　　ride

4. Bill cannot _____ a mile.　　bake　　hike　　hide

5. Val gave us a _____ melon.　　ripe　　ride　　rip

6. Did the dog save the man's _____ ?　　lift　　life　　like

---

dim　　dime　　pin　　pine　　rid　　ride

mine　　tie　　sit　　kite　　nine　　fire

_____

Directions: Read the sentence. Find the correct word from those at the right, and print it on the line.

1. We did it in a game.   rain   ran   man

2. A dog has it.   tail   pail   pat

3. We did it to Pat's cake.   at   late   ate

4. Jane has a can for it.   pat   pain   paint

5. We like to see this.   bake   mile   lake

6. A can has this.   did   died   lid

7. We like to eat it.   bit   pie   pat

8. We can ride it.   bill   bat   bike

9. Dave can put it on.   tip   tie   time

10. We can save this.   like   dime   dip

Directions: Read each sentence. Draw a ring around the answer at the right. Then draw a ring around the long **U** word in each sentence. Print the long **U** words on the lines below.

1. A red vase is blue.	Yes	No
2. A mule can kick.	Yes	No
3. A man can ride a mule.	Yes	No
4. A cube can play with a bat.	Yes	No
5. A mule has nine tails.	Yes	No
6. The five ducks are cute.	Yes	No
7. Sue can sit in the sun.	Yes	No
8. A cube has six sides.	Yes	No
9. You can eat a suit.	Yes	No
10. A tube is a top that can sing.	Yes	No
11. We can use the tire.	Yes	No
12. We can sing a tune.	Yes	No

1. _____

2. _____

3. _____

4. _____

5. _____

6. _____

7. _____

8. _____

9. _____

10. _____

11. _____

12. _____

Directions: Read the words in the list at the left. Print the short **U** words on the short **U** ladder. Print the long **U** words on the long **U** ladder.

If a one-part word or syllable has two vowels, the first vowel usually stands for a long sound, and the second is silent.

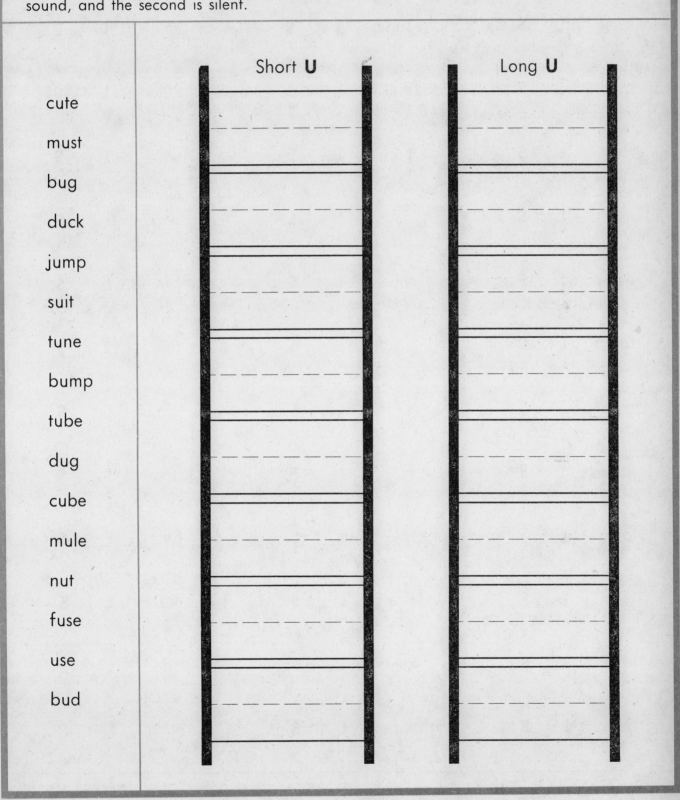

cute

must

bug

duck

jump

suit

tune

bump

tube

dug

cube

mule

nut

fuse

use

bud

Short **U**

Long **U**

Directions: Read each word below. If the word is a long-vowel word, draw a ring around the **L**. If the word is a short-vowel word, draw a ring around the **S**.

late	L	S	June	L	S	mule	L	S
man	L	S	milk	L	S	rake	L	S
rain	L	S	pick	L	S	six	L	S
use	L	S	cute	L	S	cap	L	S
bat	L	S	time	L	S	fun	L	S
suit	L	S	lick	L	S	us	L	S
map	L	S	wide	L	S	gate	L	S
tame	L	S	pie	L	S	tune	L	S
lap	L	S	ate	L	S	fill	L	S
up	L	S	fire	L	S	make	L	S
tube	L	S	cut	L	S	ride	L	S
bake	L	S	wipe	L	S	nut	L	S

Directions: Read each sentence that is started for you. Draw a ring around the word that belongs in it. Print the word on the line.

1. I paid a _____ for the nuts.   dim   dime   cat

2. Sue has _____ blue cups.   fix   fan   six

3. Dad gave Jim a red _____ .   sun   tie   sit

4. The _____ melt fast in the pop.   came   cub   cubes

5. May I use June's _____ of paste?   tub   tube   tune

6. It is _____ to get the mule.   tune   tip   time

7. We _____ milk and pie.   had   hid   suit

8. We ran fast side by _____ .   side   sum   wide

9. Mom will _____ us to the game.   like   tack   take

10. Mike likes to bake a _____ .   pin   pie   tie

Directions: First draw a ring around each long **O** word in the list. Then read each sentence that is started. Find the word that belongs in it in the list at the right. Print the word on the line.

If a one-part word or syllable has two vowels, the first vowel usually stands for a long sound, and the second is silent.

rod	road	rode	cot	coat	got	goat
hope	hop	robe	rob	coke	cost	coast

---

1. You may go home with _____ .   coat

2. See the big _____ on the lake.   Joan

3. Joan had a red hat and _____ .   rope

4. Moe has a _____ for a pet.   note

5. The dog dug a _____ for his bone.   rode

6. We _____ the bus to the big cave.   boat

7. Joe sent a _____ to his pal.   goat

8. Joan and Jay like to jump _____ .   hole

Directions: In the boxes at the top, draw a ring around the name of each picture. At the bottom, read each sentence that is started for you. The word that belongs in each sentence rhymes with the one that follows the sentence. Print the correct word on the line.

cot coat	road rod	got goat
dome dot	sap soap	rope rot

_____

- - - - - - - -

1. I _____ it will not rain for the game.   rope

   _____

   - - - - - - - -

2. Joan has a vase for the pink _____ .   nose

   - - - - - - - -

3. Joe will toss a bone to his _____ .   fog

   - - - - - - - -

4. Sue ran up the _____ to see Pam.   toad

Directions: Read the words in the first box. Use the words to find the name of each picture at the top. Print the name of each picture on the line. Then at the bottom, find the word in the list at the right that belongs in each sentence. Print the word on the line.

mail	dive
bake	five
soap	hope
tube	kite
cube	toad

1. Kate can jump _____ with Fay. _____   cake

2. The boys sat on a rock at the _____ .   rope

3. Dale will bake a date _____ .   lake

4. Kay hit the ball with the _____ .   suit

5. James put on his blue _____ .   bat

54

LESSON 26: REVIEWING LONG A, I, U, O

Directions: Read the sentence that is started for you. Draw a ring around the word that belongs in the sentence, and print it on the line.

1. Jane and Jack _____ a date cake.   mad   made

2. Jack had a big _____ of the cake.   bit   bite

3. Mom will take _____ to camp.   us   use

4. I lost a _____ on the way home.   dime   dim

5. Did you _____ the game?   wine   win

6. Ask Joan to _____ the rose on my coat.   pine   pin

7. You may _____ the pen on my desk.   use   us

8. Miss Dell sent a _____ to Mom.   not   note

9. Did you _____ the rope and the hoe?   hid   hide

10. Duke will soak in a _____ of suds.   tub   tube

Directions: In the boxes at the top, draw a ring around the name of the picture. At the bottom, read the sentences that are started for you. Find the word that belongs in the sentence, and print it on the line.

If a one-part word or syllable has two vowels, the first vowel usually stands for a long sound, and the second is silent.

set seal seed	feel fell feet	seat sat soap
heel hill heat	beets beds beads	jet jeep Jean

_____

1. Pete will feed _____ to his dog.
   met   meat   neat

2. Ken will keep the bag of _____ for his meal.
   beans   beads   bed

3. Did you see the bees _____ the hive near the road?
   lean   leaf   leave

4. Dean and Eve will meet me next _____ to go on a picnic.
   wet   weed   week

Directions: Read each sentence. Draw a ring around the long **E** word in each sentence, and print it on the line.

1. Pat fed the seal.

2. I can see Don's tent by the boat.

3. The next day Ted ate a big meal.

4. The big bug is on Jean's leg.

5. Jill rode fast in Bev's jeep.

6. I will keep the cupcake for Ben.

7. The big dog is a gift for Eve.

8. Do you feel well?

9. Fran cut the red beets for a salad.

10. Dad will roast the meat in a pan with a lid.

Directions: At the top, print the letter on the line that stands for the vowel sound you hear in the name of the picture. Then find a picture whose name contains each sound asked for, and print the numeral in the circle. At the bottom, complete the rhyming words.

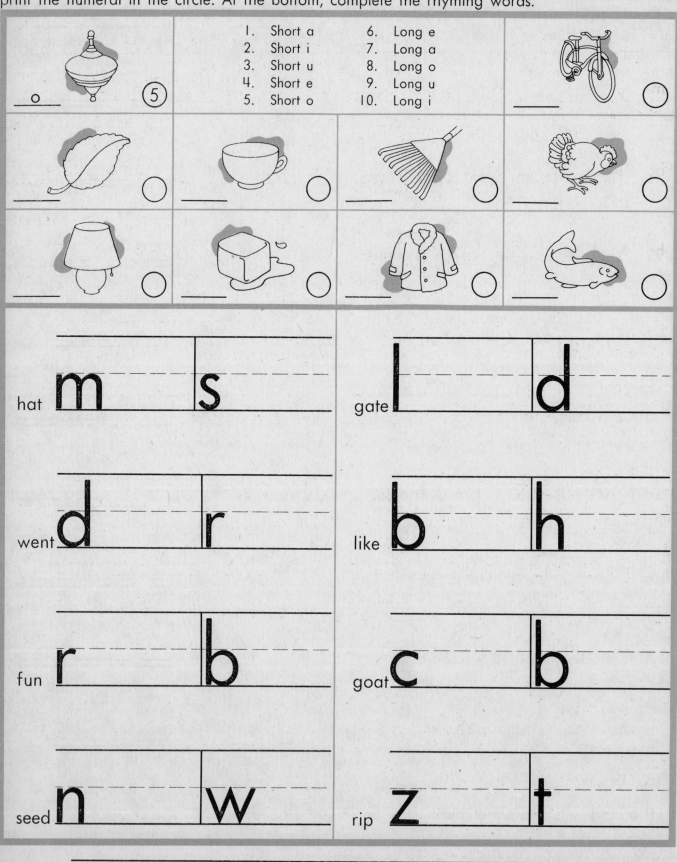

1. Short a	6. Long e
2. Short i	7. Long a
3. Short u	8. Long o
4. Short e	9. Long u
5. Short o	10. Long i

__o__   ⑤

hat   m   s

went   d   r

fun   r   b

seed   n   w

gate   l   d

like   b   h

goat   c   b

rip   z   t

Directions: At the top, change the first vowel in each word to make a new word, and print it on the line. At the bottom, find a word in column 2 that rhymes with a word in column 1, and print it on the line.

man _____   Kate _____   bake _____   had _____

boat _____   mop _____   red _____   oar _____

hop _____   run _____   cone _____   wide _____

① ②

time _____ tube

cube _____ cub

big _____ cape

rub _____ dime

need _____ dig

tape _____ feed

① ②

seat _____ tin

fin _____ heat

hope _____ cob

bet _____ rope

rob _____ late

ate _____ get

Directions: Say the name of the picture. Color the box with **S** in it if the vowel sound is short; the box with **L** if it is long. Then print the letter standing for the vowel sound you hear.

S	L		S	L		S	L		S	L
S	L		S	L		S	L		S	L
S	L		S	L		S	L		S	L
S	L		S	L		S	L		S	L

Directions: Read each sentence that is started for you. Draw a ring around the word that belongs in the sentence, and print it on the line.

1. I need a _____ for a bag of nuts. dim   dime   time

2. Pete sat in a _____ of suds. tub   rub   cub

3. The cub will not _____ you. bit   bite   kite

4. Jean's dog is _____. rut   cube   cute

5. Dad has the eggs in a _____. fox   sail   box

6. Did Tom use the blue _____? load   hole   bowl

7. Dot will sail the _____ on the lake. cot   boat   coat

8. Pam has a blue and red _____. coat   coal   cave

9. I see a lot of _____ on the desk. sail   pail   mail

10. The dog ate the _____ in the pan. met   meat   seat

Directions: At the top, take a word from the first column and put it together with a word from the second column to make a new word. Then use the new words in the sentences below.

rain	raincoat	way	oat	_____	box
sail	_____	coat	air	_____	meal
drive	_____	boat	mail	_____	plane

1. Pete will take the note to the _____.

2. The big truck rode up to the _____.

3. My _____ keeps me dry.

4. Did you see the _____ on the lake?

5. Dad gave us _____ to eat.

6. His pal gave him a ride in an _____.

62

Directions: At the top, put together two words to make a new word, and print it on the line. At the bottom, put together a syllable from the first column with one in the second to make a word. Print the word on the line.

pea weed	meal oat
sea nut	my self
cup rain	be rail
coat cake	road may

bun   et _____

tick   ny _____

tab   ny _____

pen   let _____

LESSON 30: RECOGNIZING VOWELS IN COMPOUND AND TWO-SYLLABLE WORDS

Directions: Find the word from the top of the page that belongs in each sentence. At the bottom, draw a box around each of the two little words in each compound word.

flagpole   hillside   bedtime   raincoat
teapot   cannot   inside

1. You will need your _____ .

2. Did you upset the cute _____ ?

3. The man came to paint the _____ .

4. It is _____ for Dean and Kay.

5. The goats ate the weeds on the _____ .

6. If it begins to rain, Jean and Joe will run _____ .

7. Sue _____ go with you to the picnic.

seaweed   himself   skyline   airplane

wayside   firefly   sunshine   playtime

teapot   into   itself   railroad

catnap   mailbox   treetop   birdhouse

64

Directions: Say the name of the picture. If the name has the soft sound that **C** can stand for, color the picture orange. If it has the hard sound, color it blue.

When **c** is followed by **e**, **i**, or **y**, it usually stands for a soft sound.

fence	cap	clock
cup	pencil	cake
mice	candle	celery
coat	face	rice

65

Directions: Read each sentence that is started for you. Find the word that belongs in the sentence, and print it on the line.

1. Jean and Pete will run in the _____ .

   mice   race   nice   next

2. Len put a cube of _____ in the cup.

   pink   race   face   ice

3. The five _____ ran to the hole by the fence.

   pay   mice   nice   nuts

4. As Jan ran, her _____ became red.

   coat   cement   face   cone

5. Joan likes to eat _____ with milk on it.

   lazy   lace   face   rice

6. You must find a mask for your _____ .

   face   fast   fame   fact

Directions: The letter **G** has two sounds—hard or soft. Print each word you see at the top of the page on a line in the correct column.

When **g** is followed by **e**, **i**, or **y**, it usually stands for a soft sound.

gem	goes	dog	cage	gum	good	gave	age
wage	Gene	gym	goat	giant	egg	game	page

Soft-*g* words

Hard-*g* words

Directions: Draw a blue line under each word in the list that has the hard sound of **C** or **G**. Print in a bubble each word that has the soft sound of **C** or **G**.

price

mice

goat

age

wage

games

huge

cent

gem

ice

gym

cake

cell

lunge

race

rice

gas

cone

face

giant

Directions: Print S if the word has a soft sound of **C** or **G**; print H if the word has a hard sound of **C** or **G**. At the bottom, draw a red box around each soft **G** word. Draw a blue box around each soft **C** word.

nice _____ cuff _____ ice _____ cabin _____ lunge _____ camel _____

game _____ race _____ cuff _____ age _____ came _____ coast _____

cake _____ coat _____ pencil _____ gym _____ cent _____ giant _____

gate _____ ridge _____ care _____ goes _____ recess _____ Vince _____

page _____ mice _____ rice _____ gem _____ Gail _____ care _____

1. Gail gave Vince a cage for his pet.

2. After the game they held a dance in the gym.

3. A fence ran along the ridge of the hill.

4. Gary will not budge from his seat near the TV.

5. Cindy saw the new bridge in the city.

6. The giant wildcat is at the edge of the cave.

7. A pack of gum will cost you ten cents.

8. The desk lamp casts a red dot on the yellow ceiling.

Directions: Say the name of the picture. Print the blend that stands for the sound you hear at the beginning. Then use the words to answer the five riddles.

A **Blend** is two or three consonants sounded together.

____ apes   ____ og   ____ oss   ____ ee

____ ain

You can eat me.
I may be green, blue, white, or red.
I grow on a vine.

I am _____ .

____ uit

I am green.
I am in your yard.
Birds stay in me.

_____

I am a _____ .

I am at the store.
I am good to eat.
I help make you big.

_____

I am _____ .

I can be small.
You can play with me.
I say, "Choo, choo."

_____

I am a _____ .

I can jump and hop.
You find me in a pond.
I eat bugs.

_____

I am a _____ .

Directions: At the top, draw a ring around the word that is the name of the picture. At the bottom, find the blend in each word and print the letters on the line that stand for the sound.

grapes	trim	trade	drive
grass	truck	trap	drum
grade	train	tree	drink

from	train	dress	gray
frost	truck	drapes	grass
fruit	trick	drum	grab

bring _____   brave _____   cross _____

fry _____   trick _____   brick _____

trip _____   grain _____   trade _____

grade _____   bride _____   free _____

Directions: At the top, print the blend that stands for the sound you hear at the beginning of the name of each picture. Then read the sentences that are started for you. Draw a ring around the word that belongs in each sentence, and print it on the line.

1. Cliff will ride on his red _____ .   slip   sled

2. Brad broke the blue _____ .   please   plate

3. Jean gave Glen a _____ .   plum   play

4. Deb's dog is _____ and white.   block   black

5. The _____ are in the pots.   plants   play

LESSON 34: RECOGNIZING L BLENDS

Directions: Read each riddle, and print the answer on the line. The pictures will help you. Then read each sentence at the bottom. Find the word in the list that belongs in each sentence, and print it on the line.

I tick-tock the time.
Sometimes I chime.
What am I?

_____

_ _ _ _ _ _ _ _

High up on a pole
I flap and I blow.
What am I?

_____

_ _ _ _ _ _ _ _

_____

_ _ _ _ _ _ _ _

1. Mom will use the rake on the _____ .   clap

_ _ _ _ _ _ _ _

2. My boat can _____ on the lake.   glass

_ _ _ _ _ _ _ _

3. Baby likes to _____ her hands.   float

_ _ _ _ _ _ _ _

4. The milk is in the _____ .   clock

_ _ _ _ _ _ _ _

5. Did the cut on his hand _____ ?   grass

_ _ _ _ _ _ _ _

6. A _____ tells us the time.   blocks

_ _ _ _ _ _ _ _

7. Glen made a house with his _____ .   bleed

73

Directions: Say the name of the picture. Print the blend that stands for the sound you hear at the beginning of its name.

Directions: At the top, print the name of each picture on the line. At the bottom, find the word that belongs in each sentence, and print it on the line.

_____   _____   _____   _____

1. Did you see the _____ fly over the pond?

    from   crow   frost

2. Glen's dog is _____ and white.

    blade   bleed   black

3. Brett came home and cut the _____ .

    grass   grab   grape

4. The meat is on the _____ .

    plate   play   plum

5. Fran likes to beat the _____ .

    drum   dress   drink

LESSON 36: RECOGNIZING S BLENDS

Directions: Say the name of the picture. Print the blend that stands for the sound you hear at the beginning. The list of blends will help you.

sc	st	sp	sn	squ
scr	str	sl	sm	sw

76

Directions: At the top, read each sentence that is started for you. Find the word in the list that belongs in the sentence, and print it on the line. At the bottom, draw a ring around the name of each picture.

1. Do not _____ the milk. skate

2. Green means go, and red means _____ . spill

3. Can you _____ on the ice? stop

4. Stef saw a _____ near the barn. smell

5. I can _____ those nice flowers. swim

6. Greg will dive and _____ in the lake. snake

swim   stem   scream   screen   smile   smoke

stops   steps   snake   sneak   sled   slide

Directions: Say the name of the picture. Print the blend that stands for the sound you hear at the beginning.

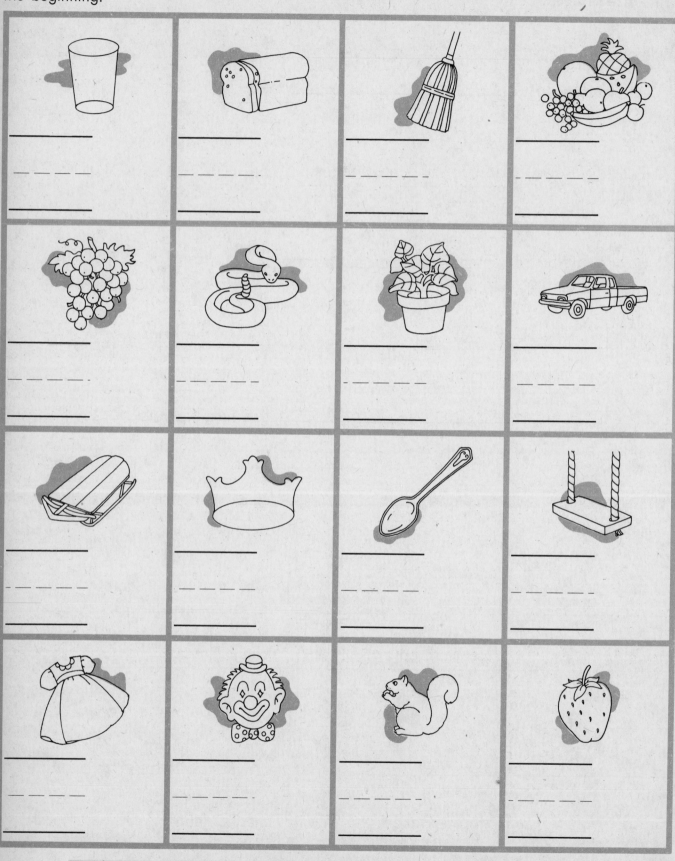

Directions: Read each sentence. Draw a ring around the blend that will complete the unfinished word. Print the blend on the line.

1. Did you win the _____ ize?   cl   sn   pr

2. Fran _____ ove the blue car.   dr   gl   sc

3. The _____ ack cat ran up the street.   squ   gr   bl

4. I will _____ ay home.   cr   fl   st

5. Do you like to eat _____ ums?   pl   fr   scr

6. I like to see the _____ ag wave.   tr   st   fl

7. Will you _____ ink the milk?   dr   sl   bl

8. I saw a _____ ane in the sky.   scr   pl   gl

9. The hill is white with _____ ow.   dr   sn   cr

10. Did you see the big _____ ake?   fr   sn   gl

Directions: Read each sentence. Change the blend in the word at the right to make a new word that belongs in the sentence. Print the word on the line.

1. Grandma likes to cut the _____ .   glass

2. We must cut the meat on the _____ .   skate

3. Do not play in the _____ .   greet

4. The robins made a nest in the _____ .   free

5. It is fun to _____ in the lake.   trim

6. I will help Fran _____ the steps.   sleep

7. Fred likes to play _____ on us.   sticks

8. I had a _____ of milk for dinner.   brass

9. Steve can _____ his top.   skin

10. Last week I had a funny _____ .   scream

Directions: At the top, find the blend that will complete the unfinished word in each sentence. Print the blend on the line. At the bottom, use the blend at the right to make a word that belongs in the sentence, and print it on the line.

1. We _____ ile when we are happy.   sn   sm   sp

2. Clem _____ oke the glass plate.   _____   sl   sk   br

3. When we ask for something we say _____ ease.   sp   pr   pl

4. The cat went up the _____ ee.   tr   fr   str

5. Gail likes to _____ im in the lake.   cr   sc   sw

1. The green _____ sat near the pond.   fr

2. We drink milk from a _____ .   gl

3. The class painted the _____ pole.   fl

4. Do not leave your _____ on the steps.   sk

5. My house is on this _____ .   str

LESSON 38: RECOGNIZING THE VOWEL SOUNDS OF Y

Directions: Draw a ring around each word in which **Y** stands for a sound almost like long **E**.

baby	cry	happy	why
try	lady	candy	tiny
Patty	sandy	shy	puppy
penny	Jimmy	funny	Billy
try	dry	buggy	my
sleepy	sunny	fly	Betty

1. Jane went to get a box of candy.

2. The puppy bumped into the tray.

3. Peggy will play with the baby.

4. Did you see the funny man cry?

5. Tom will get a bunny for his birthday.

6. Betty and Timmy will fry the fish.

7. My little puppy is in its box.

8. Kate lost a penny and a dime.

9. Andy will dry the dishes.

10. Ginny is a happy girl.

82

Directions: Draw a ring around each word in which **Y** stands for a sound almost like long **I**.

try	Teddy	sly	why	funny
bunny	dry	candy	rocky	my
Jenny	windy	by	sky	sunny
fry	fly	happy	Sally	cry
needy	lucky	shy	puppy	Billy

1. Did you see the sly fox?

2. I will try to win the prize.

3. Why did the bunny run?

4. Betty helps Tommy dry the dishes.

5. Vicky will fry eggs for lunch.

6. The puppy will try to run.

7. Gene is shy in school.

8. Have you seen my little red top?

9. See the plane fly in the sky.

10. I set the shell by the box.

Directions: Find a **Y** word at the bottom of the page that belongs in each sentence. Color each ball green that has a word with **Y** standing for a long **I** sound. Color each ball orange that has a word with **Y** standing for a long **E** sound.

1. _____ are you crying?

2. The name of the boy is _____ .

3. Tony's _____ dug a hole.

4. Molly will _____ to win.

5. The dog did a _____ trick.

Teddy   dry   funny   candy   sky

happy   fly   Why

jelly   by   puppy   try

Directions: Look at the picture in each box. Say its name. Read the words in the list. Draw a ring around each word that has the same sound of **Y** as the name of the picture.

baby	sky
my	sunny
fly	fairy
fifty	cry
bunny funny	pony Bobby

dolly	lady
try	penny
sly	shy
kitty	fry
fly dry	puppy happy

why	my
silly	sixty
baby	fly
by	Sally
lily bunny	cry sky

jelly	lucky
Sandy	try
my	fifty
fry	sky
sky cry	candy puppy

85

Directions: Read each sentence. Find a word in the column at the right that will complete the sentence, and print it on the line.

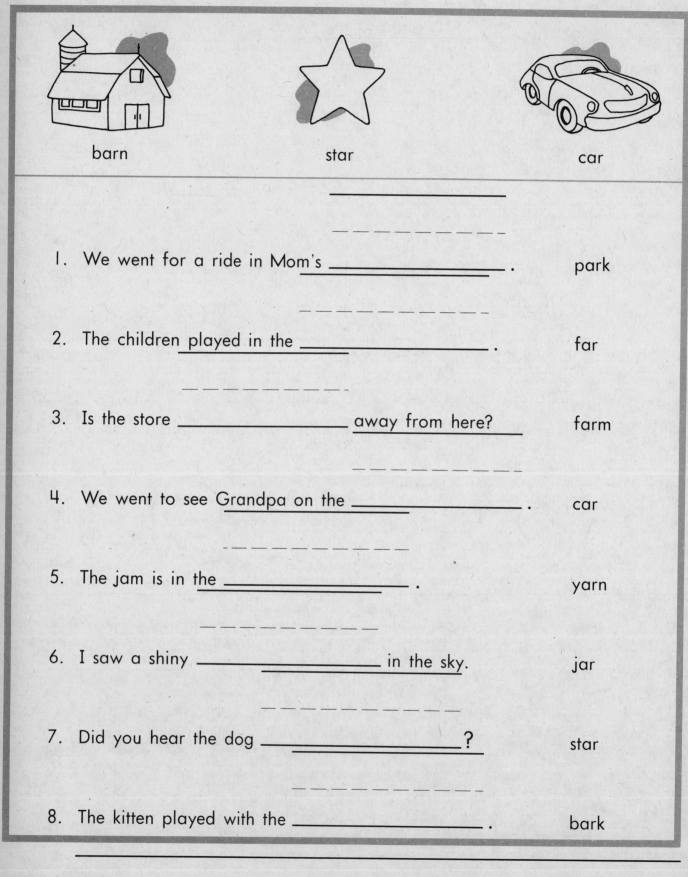

barn   star   car

_____

1. We went for a ride in Mom's _____ .   park

2. The children played in the _____ .   far

3. Is the store _____ away from here?   farm

4. We went to see Grandpa on the _____ .   car

5. The jam is in the _____ .   yarn

6. I saw a shiny _____ in the sky.   jar

7. Did you hear the dog _____ ?   star

8. The kitten played with the _____ .   bark

LESSON 40: RECOGNIZING THE SOUND OF AR

Directions: Read the word following each sentence. Change the last letter to make a new word that will finish the sentence, and print it on the line. At the bottom, print two rhyming words under each of the given words.

_____

1. Fran will mail Dan a _____ .   cart

2. Do not try to read in the _____ .   dart

3. Can you see the _____ in the sky?   start

4. We made funny cards in _____ class.   arm

5. See the goats and pigs in the _____ at the farm. bark

6. Kate and Jake went to play in the _____ .   part

7. To begin means to _____ .   stars

mark	start	hard

87

Directions: Answer each riddle by thinking of a word that rhymes with the word following the riddle. Print the word on the line.

Mark and Lori like to play word games. Do you think words are fun?

1. Something to eat.   horn   _____

2. Something on an ox.   born   _____

3. Something we eat with.   cork   _____

4. Something that brings rain.   form   _____

5. Something we play with our pals.   port   _____

6. Some place to shop.   more   _____

7. Something on a rose.   born   _____

Directions: Draw a ring around the name of the picture. Color the pictures.

jab
jar
jay

yard
yarn
yell

barn
bark
book

home
horse
horn

fifty
forty
fairy

torch
arch
scorch

car
card
cost

come
corn
cart

store
stand
star

home
horse
horn

arm
are
am

fort
farm
fork

Directions: In each list draw a ring around each word with the same sound as the name of the picture. Use the words in the lists to find the name of each picture at the bottom. Print the words on the lines.

bird	turkey	fern

ir

fork
skirt
shirt
girl

ur

purse
card
church
fur

er

letter
hammer
ruler
clerk

Directions: Draw a ring around the name of each picture. Then color the box with the same vowel with **r** as the name. Find the word that completes each sentence, and print it on the line.

	bird			first			tar	
	barn			ruler			turkey	
	burn			farm			third	

er	or	ir	ir	er	ar	ur	ar	or

	hammer			shirt			goat	
	farmer			skirt			garden	
	summer			scarf			girl	

ir	or	er	ar	ir	ur	ir	or	ur

1. The big white rabbit has white _____ .

    far
    fur
    fist

2. We can hear the birds _____ .

    church
    cheat
    chirp

3. Becky looked for her _____ .

    purse
    purple
    park

4. Peter sent me a _____ for my birthday.

    curl
    cord
    card

Directions: In each word find the vowel followed by **r**. Print the two letters next to the word. Then print the numeral of the picture that has the same two letters in its name.

1. car 2. horn 3. bird 4. hammer 5. church

part

verse

turn

perch

pork

first

party

third

storm

her

fir

burn

park

horse

fur

skirt

Directions: Draw a ring around the letters to finish the word in each sentence. Print the letters on the line. Use the words in the list to answer the riddles at the bottom.

1. The black horse is in the b _____ n.   ar   or   ur

2. My cat has gray f _____ .   or   ur   ar

3. Peggy sits in the f _____ st seat.   or   ir   ar

4. The c _____ k is in the jug.   ar   er   or

5. Kurt swept the d _____ t away.   ir   or   ar

6. The cl _____ k gave me back a dime.   ar   er   or

bark	dark	corn
skirt	fur	born
park	clerk	car

It is part of a dress.	You like to eat it.	Dogs do this.
_____	_____	_____
_____	_____	_____
A rabbit has it.	**A person can drive it.**	**We play games in it.**
_____	_____	_____
_____	_____	_____

93

Directions: Say the name of each picture. Draw a ring around the vowel followed by **r** that you hear in the name.

ar / or / ur	or / ir / ar	ar / er / or
er / or / ar	ar / er / or	or / ar / ir
ar / or / ir	or / ur / ar	er / or / ar
ur / or / ar	ar / er / or	ir / or / ar

Directions: Read the sentences and do what they tell you to do. Then draw a line under each word that has the letters **ar**, **or**, **ir**, **er**, or **ur**.

1. Do you see the skirt? Draw a ring around the skirt. Color the skirt red.

2. See the ruler. Color it green. Make a black dot near it.

3. Can you see the fern? Color it green. Draw a line under it.

4. Look at the girl. Color her hair yellow. Color her scarf blue.

5. See the barn. Make a little red **X** under it. Color the barn.

6. Do you see the corn? Color the corn yellow. Draw a box around the corn.

7. See the star. Color it blue. Make two red dots near the star.

8. Look at the turkey. Draw a black **X** on it. Color it red and purple.

Directions: Read each sentence. Find the word in the list at the top that the sentence tells about. Print it on the line.

jar

bird   purple   car

fork   farm   clerk

1. I use it when I eat.   _____

2. It makes a nest in a tree.   _____

3. A person helping in the store.   _____

4. Chickens and pigs live here.   _____

5. It is the name of a color.   _____

6. It has jam in it.   _____

7. You can ride in it.   _____

Directions: At the top, add the ending **ing** to each root word. Print the new word. At the bottom, complete each sentence by adding the ending **ing** to the word following the sentence.

sleep _____   jump _____

brush _____   play _____

help _____   start _____

hunt _____   fish _____

1. The children are _____ for the bus.   wait

2. Dora and Mark are _____ rope.   jump

3. Sue is _____ at the blue coat.   look

4. Mother is _____ Jane's hair.   brush

5. Bart is _____ to help us.   stay

Directions: In the first exercise, add the ending **ed** to each root word. In the second exercise, choose a word that you made in the first to complete each sentence. In the third exercise, print the root word on the line.

rain _____

pack _____

help _____

leap _____

ask _____

1. The frog _____ over a rock in the garden.

2. Chuck _____ fix the desk.

3. I _____ my bag for the trip.

4. Pat _____ for a big red dog.

5. It _____ on the first day.

locked _____

marched _____

dreamed _____

played _____

cleaned _____

passed _____

LESSON 45: ADDING SUFFIXES -S; -ES

Directions: Choose the correct word, and print it on the line. Color one or two pictures in each box according to your answer.

If a word ends in **x**, **z**, **ss**, **sh**, or **ch**, usually add **es** to make it mean more than one.

1. Dick broke two of Mom's yellow
dish   dishes

_____

_____ .

2. We have candy in two
box   boxes

_____

_____ .

3. Jack's mother gave him a
cap   caps

_____

_____ .

4. Look at those shiny
star   stars

_____

_____ .

5. "Peep, peep," said the two
chick   chicks

_____

_____ .

6. We like to eat fresh
peach   peaches

_____

_____ .

7. Sue will use a hair
brush   brushes

_____

_____ .

8. Just look at those
dog   dogs

_____

_____ .

9. The box was used for
mitten   mittens

_____

_____ .

10. At the zoo we saw some
seal   seals

_____

_____ .

99

Directions: At the top, add either the ending **es** or **ed** to the root word to complete each sentence. At the bottom, add the ending **s** or **es** to each root word and print it on the line.

1. Jean brush _____ her hair until it shines.

2. When Carlos miss _____ the bus, he walks.

3. The dog bark _____ when the car came near.

4. Randy cheer _____ until his throat was sore.

5. The girls play _____ ball in the school yard.

6. See the bee as it buzz _____ near the bushes.

fish   branch   mail   line

_____   _____

_____   _____

Directions: Draw a ring around the word that belongs in each sentence, and print it on the line.

1. Fred _____ the chickens.

feed
feeding
feeds

2. Day after day that truck _____ his house.

passes
passing
pass

3. A big boat is _____ on the lake.

floating
floats
floated

4. Mr. Gray went _____ after dinner.

walked
walking
walk

5. Sally _____ a puppy.

wants
want
wanting

6. He _____ faster than Billy and Dan.

work
working
worked

7. Peggy is _____ Sue with her reading.

helped
helps
helping

8. The horse likes _____ fences.

jump
jumps
jumping

9. Mother _____ for her blue pen.

look
looking
looked

10. Danny went _____ with his father.

fished
fish
fishing

Directions: At the top, add each ending to the root words. At the bottom, complete each sentence by adding the correct ending to the word following the sentence.

	s or es	ed	ing
bump	_____	_____	_____
mix	_____	_____	_____
help	_____	_____	_____
pass	_____	_____	_____

1. Norm is _____ for his mitt.   look

2. They are _____ to clean the desks.   go

3. We are _____ a good lunch.   pack

4. The boys _____ the pens to the girls.   pass

5. Pat _____ us to sing.   teach

Directions: Add the ending **ing** to the root word following each sentence. Then write the word on the line to complete the sentence.

When a short-vowel word ends in a single consonant, usually double the consonant before adding **ing**.

1. The girls were _____ to the park.   run

2. Here comes a rabbit _____ in the grass.   hop

3. Grace is _____ her pet rabbit.   feed

4. She likes to go _____ in the lake.   swim

5. Bert is _____ hot dogs for the party.   roast

6. Mary's dog is _____ for a treat.   beg

7. The boys are _____ near the lake.   jog

8. See the pony _____ down the road.   trot

9. Carl likes to go _____ with Father.   camp

Directions: At the top, add the ending **ed** to the word following the sentence and print it on the line. At the bottom, add the endings **ed** and **ing** to each word.

When a short-vowel word ends in a single consonant, usually double the consonant before adding **ed**.

1. Glenn _____ the ball.　　drop

2. Joan _____ to the little girl.　　nod

3. Lori _____ her mother for a bike.　beg

4. The big black dog _____ his tail.　wag

5. Sue _____ up her little brother.　pick

6. Jane _____ her hand into the pail.　dip

7. When the bell rang, we _____ printing.　stop

wag	clean	hop

104

Directions: Add the ending **ing** or **ed** to the words, and print the new words on the lines.

Do Not Forget—If a word ends with a silent **e**, drop the **e** before adding **ing** or **ed**.

ing	ed
hope _____	close _____
get _____	joke _____
eat _____	bake _____
drive _____	smile _____
save _____	help _____
camp _____	skate _____
sit _____	trim _____

Directions: Remember the rules. In the first exercise, add the ending **ing** to each root word. Then in the second exercise, add the ending **ed** to each root word.

Add **ing** to each word.

ride _____   fry _____

rub _____   hide _____

frame _____   dig _____

take _____   jump _____

poke _____   whip _____

Add **ed** to each word.

pin _____   rock _____

chase _____   smoke _____

march _____   bake _____

wish _____   drop _____

Directions: In the first exercise, add the ending that is above the column to each word below it. In the second exercise, add the correct ending to the root word to complete the sentence.

wave **ing**	skip **ed**	peach **s** or **es**
drop	like	cross
smile	press	tree

1. My _____ is much better this year.   read

2. Father said that I may go _____ .   swim

3. The old horse _____ home.   trot

4. We are _____ a birthday cake.   bake

5. Mr. Gray _____ five boxes of stamps.   save

6. Sally is _____ the big bus.   drive

LESSON 49: REVIEWING SUFFIXES -S; -ES; -ED; ING

Directions: In the first exercise, add the correct endings to the words in the list, and use them to complete the sentences. In the second exercise, draw a box around each root word.

skate   cut   cook

share   ask   spell

1. Mary Ann _____ the words for me.

2. Last night Jack _____ for a puppy.

3. I see children _____ on the ice.

4. Joan is _____ roses for Grandmother.

5. Each day Fred _____ his lunch with Bert.

6. Mom and Dad are _____ dinner for us.

dressed	buzzes	jumped	plays	puffed
brushing	crying	loading	boxes	dishes
cleaned	parking	wished	stayed	swimming
snapping	planned	cooking	drives	drops

108

Directions: Add the endings **ing**, **s** or **es**, and **ed** to each of the words.

ing	s or es	ed
jump		
smile		
clap		
drop		
reach		
joke		
hug		

Directions: At the top, add the ending **ful** to each root word. Then use these new words to complete the sentences below. At the bottom, draw a box around each root word.

hopeful
The ending is **ful**.
The root word is **hope**.

care _____   play _____

_ _ _ _ _ _ _ _ _ _ _   rest _____   _ _ _ _ _ _ _ _ _ _

pain _____   _ _ _ _ _ _ _ _ _ _   thank _____

_ _ _ _ _ _ _ _ _ _   _____   _ _ _ _ _ _ _ _ _ _

_ _ _ _ _ _ _ _ _ _ _ _ _ _ _

1. Jack was _____ for his gifts.

_ _ _ _ _ _ _ _ _ _ _ _ _ _ _ _ _ _

2. Be _____ when you cross the street.

_ _ _ _ _ _ _ _ _ _ _ _ _ _ _ _

3. Jean had a _____ nap.

_ _ _ _ _ _ _ _ _ _ _ _ _ _ _

4. The _____ puppy begged for food.

_ _ _ _ _ _ _ _ _ _ _ _ _ _ _ _

5. The bad tooth was _____ .

| painful | hopeful | restful | grateful |
| thankful | cheerful | playful | careful |

Directions: Add **less** or **ness** to the words at the top of the page. Then use the new words in the sentences below.

Add **less**

_____

sleep _____

care _____

harm _____

Add **ness**

_____

thick _____

neat _____

sick _____

_____

1. "He will not bite you," said Liz. "Spot is _____."

2. Ray was _____ and lost his books.

3. _____ kept Ted out of school for three weeks.

4. The _____ of his coat kept him from getting hurt.

5. The _____ baby did not take her nap.

6. Miss King gave Pat a good grade in _____.

111

Directions: At the top, add the ending **ly** to each root word. At the bottom, draw a ring around each **ly** ending in the sentences. Then print the root words on the lines.

quickly
The ending is **ly**.
The root word is **quick**.

glad _____   swift _____

soft _____   brave _____

neat _____   cruel _____

1. The children worked quickly.

2. The fireman acted bravely.

3. Mary was playing the music softly.

4. The king spoke wisely.

5. Jan and Dean have a lovely home.

Directions: In the first exercise, add the correct ending to each word in the list to make it mean more than one. In the second exercise, draw a box around each root word.

desk _____

box _____

wish _____

game _____

book _____

can _____

brush _____

glass _____

train _____

doll _____

bench _____

dish _____

school _____

peach _____

sleeping	looking	gladly	toasted
rubbing	folded	quickly	sweetly
cupful	swiftly	painted	hopping
slowly	printing	harmful	planted

Directions: In each box, match the root word in the first column with the new word in the second column. Print the correct numeral on the line.

_____ quick	1. slowly		_____ glad	1. softly
_____ sweet	2. quickly		_____ soft	2. nearly
_____ slow	3. sweetly		_____ near	3. lovely
_____ loud	4. loudly		_____ love	4. gladly
_____ use	1. playful		_____ help	1. armful
_____ play	2. handful		_____ hope	2. cupful
_____ cheer	3. useful		_____ arm	3. helpful
_____ hand	4. cheerful		_____ cup	4. hopeful
_____ home	1. cheerless		_____ care	1. fearless
_____ use	2. homeless		_____ sleeve	2. jobless
_____ wire	3. useless		_____ fear	3. careless
_____ cheer	4. wireless		_____ job	4. sleeveless
_____ like	1. sweetness		_____ good	1. softness
_____ sad	2. sickness		_____ dark	2. nearness
_____ sweet	3. likeness		_____ near	3. darkness
_____ sick	4. sadness		_____ soft	4. goodness

Directions: In the first exercise, add the ending from the list at the right to make each sentence read correctly. In the second exercise, choose a word from the list that means the same as each set of words in the columns.

_____

- - - - - - -

1. Jane is a very friend _____ girl.

- - - - -

2. It is care _____ to leave things on the steps.   **ly**

- - - - - -

3. Our kitten is very play _____ . _____   **ful**

- - - - - -

4. Our car stopped when we were near _____ home.   **less**

- - - - - -

5. Sing and play your sad _____ away.   **ness**

- - - - - -

6. We like pals who are cheer _____ .

homeless	safely	sadly	playful	harmful	helpful

no home _____   full of play _____

- - - - - - -   - - - - - - - -

with harm _____   being of help _____

- - - - - - -   - - - - - - - -

with sadness _____   in a safe way _____

- - - - - - -   - - - - - - - -

_____

- -

115

Directions: In the first exercise, add the ending to each root word. In the second exercise, add the correct ending to each root word to complete the sentence.

ly

soft _____

glad _____

ful

help _____

cheer _____

less

home _____

pain _____

ness

sad _____

sick _____

1. Spot is a very _____ pet.   play

2. The clean dishes are _____ .   spot

3. Mark will _____ help you.   glad

4. We were in _____ after the storm.   dark

5. Drink this _____ of milk.   glass

Directions: In the first exercise, add the endings **er** and **est** to each word, and print the new words on the lines. In the second exercise, draw a picture to show the meaning of each word.

	er	**est**
near		
long		
fast		
dark		
clean		
thick		
deep		
soft		

long	longer	longest

Directions: In the first exercise, add the endings **er** and **est** to the words in the list. In the second, complete each sentence by adding **er** or **est** to the root word at the right.

When a word ends in **y** after a consonant, change the **y** to **i** before adding the ending **er** or **est**.

er	est
silly	
happy	
lazy	

1. That is the _____ dog I have ever seen.   funny

2. The blue dress is _____ than the red one.   pretty

3. Mark tried to tell the _____ story.   silly

4. We must wait for a _____ day to sail.   windy

5. This road is _____ than the one we were on.   bumpy

6. Sally was the _____ one at the big fair.   lucky

Directions: Draw a ring around the name of each picture at the top. Read each sentence below. Remember the rule. Print the word that correctly completes each sentence.

When a word ends in **y** after a consonant, change the **y** to **i** before adding the ending **es**.

daisy   daisies   cherry   cherries   lily   lilies

1. Joe liked the five little circus _____ .   pony

2. Miss Day asked us to make two _____ .   copy

3. There were three _____ under the bush.   bunny

4. We picked a bunch of _____ .   daisy

5. We liked the two black _____ best.   puppy

6. Dad told us two funny _____ .   story

7. The lady gave Jay ten _____ .   penny

Directions: In the first exercise, change the words to mean more than one. In the second, circle the word that belongs in each sentence, and print it. In the third, print each picture's name.

lady _____   city _____   pony _____

_____

jelly _____   dress _____   box _____

_____

bunny _____   lily _____   candy _____

_____

1. Mary went to two birthday (party - parties). _____

2. We like to hear Vic read a (story - stories). _____

3. Nan has fifty (penny - pennies) in the bank. _____

4. There are pretty (lily - lilies) in the vase. _____

Directions: Read each sentence. Add the ending **es** to the word at the right to correctly complete the sentence.

1. We will read five new _____.   story

2. Susan picked some ripe _____.   cherry

3. Chuck went to three _____.   party

4. Cindy planted six pots of _____.   lily

5. The boy spent his ten _____.   penny

6. Can you name some big _____?   city

7. It is fun to pick _____.   berry

8. Three _____ live on this farm.   family

9. Please, may I see the six _____?   puppy

10. Five _____ trotted up the road.   pony

Directions: In the first exercise, add the endings **es** and **ed** to each word. In the second, complete the sentences by adding the ending **es** or **ed** to the root words.

When a word ends in **y** after a consonant, change the **y** to **i** before adding the ending **es** or **ed**.

	es	**ed**
study		
dry		
empty		

1. Last year Joe _____ to get good grades.   try

2. The baby _____ when it is hot.   cry

3. Carlos _____ his numbers last week.   study

4. We had _____ chicken for dinner.   fry

5. This morning Linda _____ the wastebasket.   empty

Directions: In the first exercise, print the root word of the underlined word in each sentence. In the second, change each word to mean more than one.

1. My doll sleeps and cries.

2. Father tried to shut the gate.

3. Sunday was sunnier than Thursday.

4. She was the happiest girl there.

5. Jack and I studied very hard.

6. Two ponies live on the farm.

city _____ puppy _____

berry _____ pony _____

lady _____ cooky _____

Directions: In the first exercise, print the word that means the same as the two words given. In the second exercise, print the shortened form of the two underlined words in each sentence.

---

she will   **she'll**

The short way to write **she will** is **she'll**.

---

you'll   they'll   she'll   we'll   I'll   he'll

I will _____ he will _____

we will _____ they will _____

she will _____ you will _____

---

1. I will go to the store with you. _____

2. He will mail the letters. _____

3. We will play games with Tom. _____

4. They will plant the tree. _____

5. You will have a surprise this week. _____

LESSON 55: CONTRACTIONS WITH NOT

Directions: In the first exercise, print the word that means the same as the two words given.
In the second, print the two words that mean the same as the underlined word.

can not   **can't**

The short way to write **can not** is **can't.**

can't	couldn't	weren't	don't
didn't	aren't	isn't	won't

are not _____   do not _____

did not _____   will not _____

were not _____   is not _____

could not _____   can not _____

1. Jane <u>isn't</u> going with you.   _____

2. We <u>haven't</u> a big box.   _____

3. Tim <u>didn't</u> clean the yard.   _____

4. Kathy <u>doesn't</u> need her coat.   _____

125

Directions: At the top, print the two words that mean the same as the shortened form. At the bottom, print the shortened form of the two underlined words in each sentence.

is	**have**
he's _____	I've _____
that's _____	you've _____
it's _____	we've _____
she's _____	they've _____

1. <u>You have</u> never been late for school. _____

2. <u>It is</u> fun to swim in the lake. _____

3. <u>I have</u> seen a rainbow. _____

4. <u>He is</u> smiling at the funny joke. _____

5. <u>That is</u> the rule for the game. _____

Directions: At the top, print the two words that mean the same as the underlined word in the sentence. At the bottom, print the word that means the same as the two words.

1. <u>We're</u> going to pick some berries. _____

2. <u>Let's</u> go on the bus. _____

3. <u>I'm</u> going to take a basket. _____

4. "<u>They're</u> baked," Tom cried. _____

5. <u>We'll</u> go to the picnic today. _____

6. <u>You're</u> the one she asked for. _____

you are _____   she is _____

I am _____   it is _____

let us _____   they are _____

we are _____   we will _____

Directions: Print the numeral of each shortened form in front of the two words that have the same meaning. Then circle the word that completes each sentence, and write it on the line.

1. we're	___	I am	9. don't	___	is not
2. you'll	___	we are	10. she's	___	you are
3. it's	___	will not	11. you're	___	I will
4. can't	___	he is	12. isn't	___	we will
5. I'm	___	you will	13. she'll	___	do not
6. he's	___	let us	14. we'll	___	I have
7. won't	___	can not	15. I'll	___	she will
8. let's	___	it is	16. I've	___	she is

1. Why _____ you skate with Carla and me?

      isn't
      don't
      you're

2. The sick girl _____ walk to the park.

      isn't
      can't
      don't

3. I will help you if _____ play with the baby.

      you'll
      it's
      she's

4. Mother said, " _____ take you shopping."

      I'll
      won't
      she's

Directions: Print the shortened form of the two words that are underlined in each sentence.

1. He will read a story to the class.

2. Let us start the baseball game.

3. You are very helpful to the sick lady.

4. Jane has not missed a day of school.

5. He is feeling well today.

6. I will help you if you will let me.

7. Jean can not skate very well.

8. It is time to go to school.

9. Grace will not wait for the girls.

10. Gus is not going to play with us.

Directions: At the top, print the shortened form of the two words that are underlined. At the bottom, print the two words that mean the same as the shortened form.

1. <u>You are</u> a good reader, Jess.

2. <u>You will</u> have to hurry home for lunch.

3. <u>We are</u> going to the park to play games.

4. <u>Let us</u> do our work neatly.

5. <u>I have</u> hired five more girls.

I've _____   didn't _____

he'll _____   you've _____

they're _____   let's _____

isn't _____   won't _____

Directions: At the top, print the shortened form that means the same as the two words. At the bottom, draw a ring around the correct word, and print it on the line.

I have _____   can not _____

do not _____   could not _____

let us _____   there is _____

1. _____ a surprise for Lee.   Didn't   It's

2. _____ my new bike.   That's   Isn't

3. Beth _____ be here today.   won't   it's

4. Jack _____ get in the game.   didn't   it's

5. _____ the first one here.   Let's   You're

6. _____ my best baseball.   That's   Won't

7. He _____ need my help.   aren't   doesn't

Directions: Read the sentence. Find the word in the list that each sentence tells about, and print it on the line.

> If a one-part word or syllable has two vowels, the first vowel is usually long and the second one is silent.

chain	stain	mailbox	hay
pail	rain	hair	paint
chair	train	gray	sail

1. I ride on railroad tracks. _____

2. You drop letters in me. _____

3. If I start, you put on a raincoat. _____

4. You can sit on me. _____

5. I am made of many links. _____

6. I am part of a boat. _____

7. I am an ink spot on a shirt. _____

8. I am piled in a stack. _____

Directions: Find the word in the list that completes each sentence. Print it on the line. Then print the two vowels that stand for a long **e** sound.

sleeve	beads	street	tree
read	meat	deer	team

1. Bruce likes to _____ this story. _____

2. Clean the spot off your _____ . _____

3. I'll help you string the blue _____ . _____

4. Look before you cross the _____ . _____

5. Pat has seen a _____ near the camp. _____

6. The dog ate the _____ in the dish. _____

7. The baseball _____ played hard. _____

8. This _____ has ripe peaches. _____

Directions: In the first exercise, print the numeral of the picture in the correct box. In the second exercise, draw a ring around the correct word, and print it on the line.

[ ] hoe [ ] soap [ ] tie [ ] toad [ ] pie [ ] coal [ ] road [ ] boat

1   2   3   4

5   6   7   8

1. Frank cut his _____ on the sharp rock.   hoe   load   toe

2. Judy made a _____ for her sister.   catch   came   coat

3. We ate peach _____ at the party.   tie   die   pie

4. _____ will pay for the donut.   toe   Joe   toad

5. Spot ran down the _____ to meet Dad.   road   rod   ride

6. Randy _____ the string on the kite.   cried   tied   fry

134

LESSON 58: REVIEWING REGULAR DOUBLE VOWELS AI; AY; EE; EA; OA; IE; OE'

Directions: At the top, draw a ring around the word to complete each sentence. Print it on the line. At the bottom, choose the correct double vowel from the right to complete the word in each sentence, and print it on the line.

1. Hear the frogs _____ . croak coat coal

2. Kay baked some _____ for us. ties cries pies

3. The pepper made me _____ . steal sneeze spear

4. We need to _____ the trees. spray tray stay

5. The farmer lost a _____ . weep sheep deep

1. Joe stubbed his big t _____ . **ai**

2. I just had a slice of t _____ st. **ay**

  ee

3. Jay, may I keep your pen all d _____ ? **ea**

  oa

4. The hose sprang a l _____ k. **ie**

  oe

5. Ann broke the ch _____ n on her bike.

135

Directions: Find the name of each picture in the list at the top of the page. Print it on the line.

rain	hoe	pie	beet	hay	tree
leaf	deer	boat	daisy	nails	feet

Directions: At the top, print the numeral of the answer in each box. At the bottom, make a word to answer each riddle by adding beginning and ending letters.

The farmer feeds the ☐ .

Jenny's boat can ☐ on the lake.

A ☐ can be used to dig in a garden.

Father said, "Use ☐ on your hands."

Baby ☐ when she broke her doll.

Glenn picked a ripe ☐ from the tree.

Grandma made a blackberry ☐ .

We will help ☐ the house.

Farmer Gray planted ☐ in spring.

1. soap
2. sheep
3. hay
4. float
5. hoe
6. pie
7. paint
8. cried
9. peach

1. It fell from the tree. ___ ___ ea ___ ___

2. It is something to put on. ___ oa ___

3. A dog wags it. ___ ai ___

4. Farmers use them in gardens. ___ oe ___

5. We like to eat them. ___ ie ___

6. We stand on them. ___ ee ___

Directions: At the top, print the name for each picture below it. At the bottom, choose the correct word, and print it on the line.

snow	rainbow	snowman	bow	crow	bowl

1. Nora played in the _____ yesterday.   snow   mow

2. Dad used his truck to _____ the car.   row   tow

3. Please pass the _____ of fruit.   bowl   bow

4. The black _____ flies past the window.   grow   crow

5. Can you _____ the ball to the tree?   throw   grow

138

LESSON 60: RECOGNIZING VOWEL DIGRAPH OO

Directions: Draw a ring around the correct word, and print it on the line.

1. May I sweep the _____ for you?   moon   shoot   room

2. Benny swept the steps with a _____ .   soon   broom   boom

3. Glenn had a loose _____ .   tooth   spoon   broom

4. Fran swam in the _____ each day.   cool   pool   tool

5. The lake water was _____ .   stool   spool   cool

6. At _____ we eat lunch at school.   spoon   noon   moon

7. Mary sat on the _____ to read.   stool   pool   cool

8. Father took us to the _____ .   too   moo   zoo

9. We are looking for the _____ chest.   tool   fool   drool

10. We saw a _____ at the farm.   soothe   goose   boom

LESSON 60: RECOGNIZING VOWEL DIGRAPH OO

Directions: In the first exercise, draw a ring around the correct word, and print it on the line. In the second exercise, print the name of the picture and a word that rhymes with it.

_____

1. Tammy _____ the plum tree.   look   shook   hook

2. Will you chop the _____?   wood   hood   took

3. We can wade in the _____.   book   cook   brook

4. Tony _____ out his books.   good   took   stood

5. Put the coat on the _____.   hook   look   shook

6. Show the _____ to Tom.   look   good   book

7. Carla _____ up and looked.   took   stood   good

| b | h | h | w |
| sh | st | br | g |

140

Directions: In the first exercise, find the correct word to complete each sentence. In the second exercise, draw a ring around the correct word.

1. We wanted _____ for supper.   ready

2. My purse is made of brown _____ .   head

3. Are you _____ for school today?   bread

4. Grandmother needed more _____ .   sweater

5. Tom fell and bumped his _____ .   breath

6. It is cool, so you need your white _____ . thread

7. When it is cold you can see your _____ .   leather

1. In the morning you eat (breading, breakfast, breathing).

2. In the big, green (sweater, weather, meadow) we saw the sheep.

3. The (head, lead, thread) in my pencil broke.

4. The (feather, weather, leather) today is cool.

5. Zeke uses (cleanser, feathers, bread) to clean the tub.

Directions: In the first exercise, print the numeral of the answer in the box in front of each riddle. In the second exercise, draw a ring around the name of each picture.

☐	Something we use for sweeping.	1. bread
☐	A food we can eat with each meal.	2. blow
☐	Something we read in school.	3. sweater
☐	You can do this to a horn.	4. broom
☐	Something that shines when it is dark.	5. book
☐	Something to put on when it is cool.	6. spread
☐	Something for a bed.	7. stool
☐	Something we see during winter.	8. rooster
☐	Something to sit on.	9. moon
☐	A bird that crows.	10. snow

headline headstone	stool spoon	weather sweater	stool pool
bread thread	peacock peaceful	booth broom	feather leather

142

LESSON 61: REVIEWING REGULAR DOUBLE VOWELS; VOWEL DIGRAPHS

Directions: At the top, circle the correct word and print it on the line. At the bottom, find the two vowels in each word that make one sound. Print them on the line.

1. Did you _____ the dinner?

book
cook
coop

2. There was a _____ of candy on the tray.

boot
bowl
snow

3. Dean bumped his _____ on the shelf.

head
heap
lead

4. The children begged to swim in the _____.

pool
wool
poor

5. These men eat lunch at _____.

room
roof
noon

6. We took the _____ stone across the road.

heavy
lead
leave

moon _____   hoop _____   tea _____   float _____   deaf _____

leave _____   coat _____   slow _____   book _____   meat _____

bow _____   team _____   wood _____   bread _____   zoo _____

Directions: Find the correct word, and print it on the line to complete each sentence.

saw	auto	paw

_____

- - - - - - - -

1. I helped cut the green _____ .   fawn

- - - - - - -

2. A baby deer is a _____ .   saw

- - - - - - -

3. Baby can _____ on the floor.   lawn

- - - - - - -

4. Sue and Bob cut the wood with a _____ .   claws

- - - - - - -

5. The bird can scratch with its _____ .   laws

- - - - - - -

6. We drink milk with a _____ .   because

- - - - - - -

7. We must obey the _____ .   straw

- - - - - - - -

8. We left the picnic _____ of the rain.   crawl

Directions: Read each sentence, and print the correct word on the line. The words in the balloons will help you.

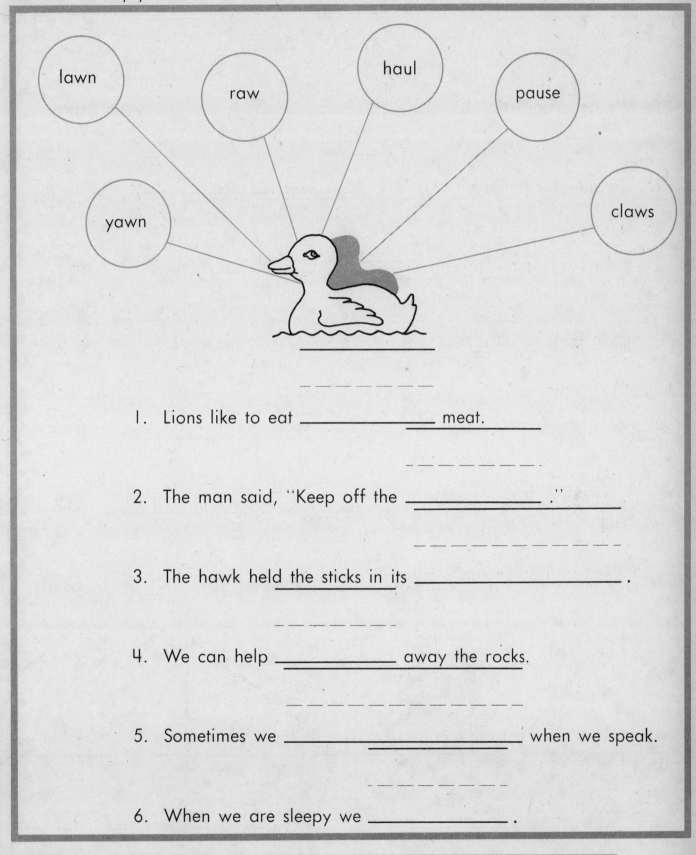

lawn

raw

haul

pause

claws

yawn

1. Lions like to eat _____ meat.

2. The man said, "Keep off the _____ ."

3. The hawk held the sticks in its _____ .

4. We can help _____ away the rocks.

5. Sometimes we _____ when we speak.

6. When we are sleepy we _____ .

LESSON 63: REVIEWING REGULAR DOUBLE VOWELS; VOWEL DIGRAPHS

Directions: In the first exercise, use a word from the list at the right to complete each sentence. In the second exercise, print the name of each picture on the line.

_____

1. We get wool from _____. gray

2. The milk for the kitten was in the _____. raining

3. We read a good story in _____ today. peas

4. Jean ate a _____ with her lunch. bowl

5. Mary has a _____ coat. peach

6. I put on my boots when it is _____. school

7. We planted _____ in the garden. sheep

_____ _____ _____ _____

146

Directions: Complete each sentence by printing on the line the correct word from the list.

1. Mother gave Grace a big _____ to eat.   train

2. Baby likes to _____ with her doll.   crow

3. The little red choo-choo _____ stopped on the track.   books

4. Mark _____ ten books last summer.   rooster

5. Judy can _____ her yellow boat.   peach

6. The red _____ woke us up this morning. sail

7. The black _____ roosted in the tree.   Please

8. Children like to look at funny _____ .   play

9. _____ , may I pet the puppy?   green

10. The grass is pretty and _____ .   read

147

Directions: Look at the picture and say its name. Find its name in the list of words, and print the numeral of the word in the box. Color the pictures.

1. clown
2. cowboy
3. mouse
4. shower
5. howl
6. owl
7. now
8. crown
9. cloud
10. cow
11. towel
12. flowers
13. house
14. mouth
15. gown
16. pouch
17. shout
18. town

Directions: At the top, look at the picture and say its name. Notice how its name is spelled. At the bottom, find the **ou** and the **ow** words in the sentences. Print them on the lines.

crown

cow

cloud

1. There are many clouds in the sky today.

2. How many children played games?

3. The birds will fly south.

4. The car went around the block.

5. The funny clown danced to the drum.

6. Craig and the Scouts went camping.

7. The girls jumped up and down.

Directions: Read each riddle. Find the correct answer in the list of words at the top, and print it on the line.

owl   cow   house   clown   flower   cloud   plow   ground

1. I am in the sky.
Sometimes I bring you rain.
What am I?

_____

_____

2. I am in the garden.
I am very colorful.
Maybe I grow in your yard, too.
What am I?

_____

_____

3. I am wide awake in the dark.
I hoot and howl.
What am I?

_____

_____

4. You stay in me.
I keep the wind and rain
from you.
What am I?

_____

_____

5. You can plant seeds in me.
The farmer must plow me.
What am I?

_____

_____

6. I have a funny suit.
I do many tricks.
I can make you smile.
What am I?

_____

_____

7. You can see me at the farm.
I eat green grass.
I give you good milk.
What am I?

_____

_____

8. The farmer uses me.
I help him make his garden.
What am I?

_____

_____

Directions: At the top, print an X next to each word in which **ow** stands for the long **o** sound. At the bottom, draw a ring around each **ow** word. Then print an X in the column to show the sound the **ow** word has.

_____ how	_____ snow	_____ gown
_____ own	_____ town	_____ crowd
_____ now	_____ bowl	_____ grow
_____ low	_____ plow	_____ power
_____ owl	_____ slow	_____ flow
_____ know	_____ show	_____ brown
_____ crow	_____ crown	_____ down

		long vowel	diphthong
1.	The clown fell off the big box.	_____	_____
2.	Ann tied a green bow on the box.	_____	_____
3.	The cowboy rode a white horse.	_____	_____
4.	Jim cut the pretty flower.	_____	_____
5.	Mary went downtown.	_____	_____
6.	Can you eat a bowl of popcorn?	_____	_____

Directions: Draw a ring around the name of each picture. Then complete the sentences at the bottom of the page.

boy / boil / bill	boy / rag / toy	corn / coil / coins
sail / sell / soil	oak / oil / out	toil / tail / toys
paint / point / pail	noise / nail / nose	came / coil / coin

1. The _____ train is in the big box.   coins

2. I have _____ in my purse.   toy

152

Directions: Read the story. Draw a ring around each **oi** word and a box around each **oy** word. Then answer the questions at the bottom of the page.

The Little Toy Train

There was a little boy named Roy. His mom and dad gave him a toy train for his birthday. This made Roy a very happy little boy.

Roy took very good care of his toy train. Each time he used the train he oiled it. This made the toy train go fast.

But one day Roy oiled it too much. The toy train went faster and faster. It went so fast that Roy could not catch it.

Roy chased the toy train out the back door and down the path. But he could not catch it.

Baby was sitting on the grass. The toy train went to her and stopped. Baby was very happy. "Now I have a toy train," she said as she picked it up.

Roy said, "Baby, you have my toy train. It ran away from me. I used too much oil."

Baby gave Roy his toy train.

"Thank you, Baby," said Roy. "I will not spoil my toy train again by oiling it too much. From now on I will be more careful."

1. What was the little boy's name? _____

2. What did he get for his birthday? _____

3. What made the train go fast? _____

153

Directions: Find the correct word and print it on the line to complete each sentence.

1. Mary Ann will not _____ her new toy.   point   spoil   said

2. Do not put _____ near the fire.   boil   laid   oil

3. Al is going to _____ the Boy Scouts.   join   joint   jail

1. A pencil has a _____ .   toy

2. Mom puts _____ in her car.   boiling

3. The water is _____ on the stove.   oil

4. Six _____ will join the coin club.   point

5. The _____ boat has a big red sail.   boys

154

Directions: At the top, answer each question by drawing a ring around the word **yes** or **no**. At the bottom, complete each sentence by printing the correct word from the list.

1. Is a penny a coin?   Yes   No
2. Is Ann a boy's name?   Yes   No
3. Can you play with a toy drum?   Yes   No
4. Is oil used in a car?   Yes   No
5. Is a point the same as paint?   Yes   No
6. Can you boil water?   Yes   No

1. A pin has a sharp _____ on it.   spoiled

2. We will _____ eggs for breakfast.   noise

3. The _____ little girl began to pout.   boil

4. Joyce will _____ the trip to the circus.   point

5. The _____ found the owner of the stray dog.   enjoy

6. The loud _____ of the jets hurts my ears.   boy

Directions: At the top, complete each sentence by finding the correct word in the list. At the bottom, print two words that rhyme with each of the given words.

_____

- - - - - - - -

1. Sally scored a _____ points in the game.   crew

- - - - - - - - -

2. The wind _____ the trees down.   grew

- - - - - - - - -

3. You have a pretty _____ dress.   stew

- - - - - - - - -

4. The grass was wet with _____ .   few

- - - - - - - -

5. Many flowers _____ in the garden.   dew

- - - - - - - - - -

6. We ate _____ for dinner.   blew

- - - - - - - - -

7. The ship's _____ stopped in port.   new

few	crew	grew
bl	ch	dr
st	thr	fl

Directions: Draw a ring around the word that completes each sentence.

1. Liz has a (new, drew, grew) green bike.

2. The red flowers (few, threw, grew) in the garden.

3. Grandmother gave me a (crew, few, mew) pennies.

4. Matt (stew, threw, screw) the bag to Tom.

5. We had hot (few, stew, flew) for our supper.

6. I need a (few, dew, mew) children to help me.

7. You must (flew, chew, grew) your food.

8. The wind (blew, brew, new) the leaves.

9. The baby bird (threw, screw, flew) from its nest.

1. A kitten can (mew, new, blew).

2. Ted (few, drew, grew) a picture of a house.

3. The wind (flew, threw, blew) my new hat away.

4. Do you like to (few, new, chew) gum?

5. Who gave that (mew, new, threw) kite to you?

6. I use my teeth to (new, chew, few) food.

7. The campers saw (new, mew, dew) on the tent.

8. Mother read the (news, pews, dews).

9. Jill (threw, chew, few) a snowball across the street.

Directions: Read each sentence. Print a word that answers the riddle and contains the two given letters. At the bottom, complete each of the words using only the letters **ew**, **oi**, **ou**, or **ow**.

1. It is a name for money.   oi _____

2. It is something a king has.   ow _____

3. It is something we play with.   oy _____

4. It means "not used."   ew _____

5. It means "not in."   ou _____

ew   oi   ou   ow

c _____   scr _____   n _____ se   sp _____ l

h _____   c _____ nt   cr _____ d   c _____ n

dr _____   h _____ se   cl _____ n   j _____ n

f _____   s _____   th   sh _____ t   n _____ s

Directions: Find the word in the list that completes each sentence. Print it on the line.

1. Mike _____ his new tin horn loudly.   house

2. Mary put the ten _____ in her bank.   towel

3. We keep a clean _____ in the kitchen.   points

4. We may win the game by two _____ .   blew

5. Maria is playing in the _____ next door.   coins

1. My desk in school is missing one _____ .   toy

2. Roy gave me a _____ mitt.   screw

3. How much _____ did the car need?   new

4. We clapped when the _____ did funny tricks.   oil

5. What _____ will you choose for Sally's birthday?   clown

Directions: Read each riddle, and draw a box around the correct word. At the bottom of the page, draw a ring around each **ow** word in the poem.

1. You use it when you talk.
   spoil   joy   soil   voice

2. It means that something is wet.
   round   join   moist   oil

3. You see him do funny tricks.
   crown   clown   brown   cloud

4. You can live in it.
   house   mouse   plow   proud

5. It is something you do with gum.
   blew   flew   chew   crew

6. It is something a dog can do.
   howl   coin   stew   new

7. A car needs it.
   joy   boil   plow   oil

8. It is something a baby likes.
   owl   toy   crowd   how

9. It is something we can eat.
   mew   drew   stew   few

10. You can bake with it.
    owl   gown   flour   round

11. It means "not many."
    new   few   dew   stew

12. It means "dirt."
    soil   coil   boy   oil

13. The farmer uses it.
    frown   plow   down   cloud

14. The cat runs after it.
    house   shout   out   mouse

Just for Fun

"Moo-Moo," said Mother Cow.

"Give me my dinner now."

"Not now, Mother Cow,

It is time for me to plow."

160

Directions: Think of a word to complete each sentence that rhymes with the word at the right. At the bottom of the page, draw a ring around each **oi** word and each **oy** word.

1. I can hear Billy shout with _____ .   toy

2. Three _____ sat in the tree at dark.   howls

3. All the robins flew _____ .   mouth

4. Our green grass was wet with _____ .   mew

5. The rain will _____ the picnic.   oil

6. The cake needs two cups of _____ .   our

7. Jane has a _____ nuts in the bag.   dew

8. The lemon has a _____ taste.   flour

Roy enjoys toys.

Roy enjoys noise.

So Roy likes the toys

That make a loud noise.

LESSON 69: TEST: DIPHTHONGS

Directions: Find the word in the list that completes each sentence. Print it on the line.

1. On hot days the meat may _____.   toy

2. My bank is filled with _____.   spoil

3. Baby likes her new _____.   coins

4. Did you hear that _____?   house

5. Bob Brown will sell his brick _____.   noise

---

1. When you jump rope it is fun to _____.   sound

2. Please _____ water for tea.   new

3. Dad needs a _____ and a bar of soap.   count

4. A strange _____ came from the house.   towel

5. Her coat looks as good as _____.   boil

162

Directions: At the top, draw a ring around the word that completes each sentence. At the bottom, print three words from the list that begin with **ch**, **wh**, **th**, and **sh**.

1. Vic and Joe like to eat   cheese.   sheets.   chase.
2. We played in the sand at the   bunch.   bench.   beach.
3. We will paint the house   wheeze.   whine.   white.
4. Did you brush your   then?   teeth?   there?
5. We went to the pet   shop.   shone.   thin.
6. In my lunch I have a big   cheek.   with.   peach.
7. I help wash the   dash.   splashes.   dishes.

ch

th

wh

sh

Directions: Draw a ring around the word that will complete each sentence.

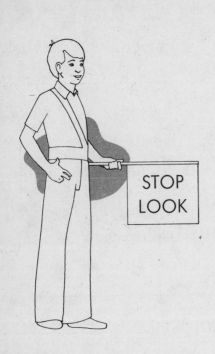

1. I hope the sun will (shine, chin).

2. (Where, This) did you go?

3. Mother wants us to (thing, think).

4. I (chose, chair) the big prize.

5. (This, When) is my best work.

6. Please get (that, what) glass.

7. (What, That) time is it?

8. (They, The) are here.

9. We will go (when, then) the bell rings.

10. Did you have (church, chicken) for dinner?

11. Have you had a ride on a (chip, ship)?

12. Do not drop that (dish, wish).

13. Sally likes to play with the (blocks, docks).

14. Will you (dish, brush) my suit?

15. Bill did not (catch, pinch) the ball.

16. We went to the (chop, shop).

Directions: If the consonant digraph is at the beginning of a word, print the word in the first column. If it is in the middle, print the word in the second. If it is at the end, print the word in the third column.

cheer	quack	reach	stuck	riches	when
shine	brushing	kicking	peach	dishes	thank
wishing	teaching	fish	bench	why	chin

BEGINNING	MIDDLE	END

Directions: Say the name of each picture. Draw a ring around the letters that stand for the digraph you hear.

th sh ck ch wh	th sh ck ch wh	th sh ck ch wh
th sh ck ch wh	th sh ck ch wh	th sh ck ch wh
th sh ck ch wh	th sh ck ch wh	th sh ck ch wh
th sh ck ch wh	th sh ck ch wh	th sh ck ch wh

Directions: Read the sentences. Then print the number of the sentence that tells about the picture in the circle below it. At the bottom, find the word in the list that answers each riddle.

1. John has a knot in the rope.
2. I know what is in the box.
3. Joan can turn the knob.

○   ○

1. Tad needs a patch on his knee.
2. Mother cut it with a knife.
3. Thad will knock down the pile.

○   ○

1. Carl has a knapsack.
2. Joe knocks on the door.
3. Grandmother likes to knit.

○   ○

_____
_ _ _ _ _ _ _ _ _ _ _

1. Something that is sharp.   _____
_ _ _ _ _ _ _ _ _ _ _

2. Something Grandmother did with the yarn.   _____
_ _ _ _ _ _ _ _ _ _ _

3. Something that is a part of your leg.   _____

| knife | knot | know | knit | knob | knee |

167

Directions: At the top, find the word that completes each sentence, and print it on the line. At the bottom, think of a **kn** word that rhymes with each of the given words.

_____

1. Nan will tie the rope in a _____ .   knit   knot

2. Put the _____ with the plate.   knife   knit

3. There was a _____ at the door.   know   knock

4. The door has a shiny brass _____ .   knob   knit

5. Jack cut it with his _____ .   knit   knife

6. Bob fell and hurt his _____ .   knee   knob

snow	sit	feel
block	wife	blew
cob	see	hot

Directions: Find the name of each picture in the list of words. Print the name on the line below the picture.

apple	eagle	needle	people
candle	turtle	handle	thimble
steeple	marble	table	bubbles

LESSON 72: RECOGNIZING WORDS ENDING IN LE

Directions: Find the word that completes each sentence, and print it on the line.

1. The _____ is boiling on the stove.   pickle

2. Red and blue make _____ .   kettle

3. The _____ of the hammer is made of wood.   puddle

4. Jack tried to jump over the _____ but fell in.   purple

5. The dill _____ made my mouth water.   handle

1. Linda likes to _____ the baby.   candles

2. Please try not to _____ when I cut your hair.   turtle

3. I lit the _____ on the cake.   wiggle

4. The _____ is the king of birds.   tickle

5. The _____ can go into its shell.   eagle

Directions: Find the word that completes each sentence, and print it on the line.

wrap   **wren**   **write**

_____

1. Ed and Dan will _____ the big surprise gift.   wrote

2. Five of my spelling words were _____ .   wren

3. Who _____ that letter to you?   wreck

4. Two new cars were in a _____ .   wrong

5. The _____ sat on her eggs in the nest.   wrap

6. When Jean fell she broke her _____ .   write

7. Sue will _____ a letter to her sister.   wrist

Directions: Find the answer to each riddle in the list of words at the top. Print the answer next to the correct numeral at the bottom.

wren	wrecker	wrapper	wrist
wrench	wreath	writer	typewriter

1. I am round and green.
   I am put on the door.
   What am I?

2. I am a little bird.
   I like to sing.
   What is my name?

3. I am part of the arm.
   I can twist and turn.
   What am I called?

4. I am a big truck.
   I tow away cars.
   What am I called?

5. I am made of paper.
   I keep candy clean.
   What am I called?

6. I am a useful tool.
   I can fix things.
   What is my name?

7. I can print.
   People strike my keys.
   What is my name?

8. I am one who writes.
   I make up stories.
   What am I called?

1. _____   5. _____

2. _____   6. _____

3. _____   7. _____

4. _____   8. _____

Directions: Find the word that completes each sentence, and print it on the line.

knows	wrapped	knock	wrong
written	knitted	doorknob	wring

_____

1. We had to _____ out our wet suits.

2. Cathy _____ some red-and-white socks.

3. The clerk _____ the gift in dark blue paper.

4. Mary _____ how to add and subtract.

5. Did you _____ at the front door?

6. Your work is neatly _____ .

7. The _____ is made of brass.

8. It is _____ to tell a lie.

Directions: Say the name of each picture. Listen for the consonant digraphs. Do you hear them at the beginning, middle, or end? Print the digraphs in the correct blocks.

Directions: Read each riddle. Find the answer in the list at the right, and print the numeral of the answer on the line.

It is something we can eat. _____   1. sheet

It is on your bed. _____   2. brush

You can sit on it. _____   3. whale

It is something we can use to clean. _____   4. chair

It lives in the sea. _____   5. peach

It is wrong to do this. _____   1. teeth

A car runs on them. _____   2. rattle

A king sits on this. _____   3. wheels

We must brush them every day. _____   4. cheat

A baby likes to play with it. _____   5. throne

You may see these on the beach. _____   1. wheat

The baker makes bread from this. _____   2. peaches

They are red and yellow and grow on trees. _____   3. shells

It is on top of a house. _____   4. clock

It tells time. _____   5. chimney

Directions: Add **re** to each word, and use the new word to complete the sentence.
When the prefix **re** is added, the meaning of the word changes. It means to **do again.**

reread
The prefix is **re**.
The root word is **read**.

_____

1. Take this clean paper and _____ your letter.   write

2. Peggy wants to _____ this book to her sister.   read

3. Jim will _____ the beds after lunch.   make

4. I have to _____ my camera.   load

5. The farmer must _____ his corn patch.   plant

6. Grandma is going to _____ her trunk.   pack

7. Now you may _____ the package for Carla.   wrap

8. Dad is going to _____ Dick's bedroom.   paint

Directions: Add **un** to each word, and use the new word to complete the sentence.
When the prefix **un** is added, the meaning of the word is changed to mean just the opposite.

The beads are strung.   The beads are unstrung.

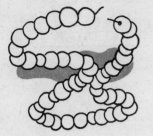

unstrung
The prefix is **un**.
The root word is **strung**.

_____

- - - - - - - - - - - - - - -

1. I will _____ my doll and put her to bed.   dress
    _____

- - - - - - - - - - - - - - -

2. Rick was _____ and shared his candy.   selfish
    _____

- - - - - - - - - - - -

3. Cindy had to _____ the gym door for the class.   lock
    _____

- - - - - - - - - - - - - -

4. When Burt broke his toy he was _____.   happy

- - - - - - - - - - - - -

5. I will _____ the knot in the string.   tie
    _____

- - - - - - - - - - - -

6. It is _____ to cheat in a game.   fair
    _____

- - - - - - - - - - - - - -

7. The gifts lay _____ on the desk.   opened

Directions: At the top, add **re** or **un** to each word, and use the new word to complete the sentence. At the bottom, print the word that means the same as the two words given.

_____

_ _ _ _ _ _ _ _ _ _

1. Please _____ the story about the dragon. read

_ _ _ _ _ _ _ _ _ _ _ _

2. You'll have to wait before you _____
   your gifts. _____   wrap

_ _ _ _ _ _ _ _ _ _ _

3. Betty will _____ the letter.   send

_ _ _ _ _ _ _ _ _ _

4. Sandy was _____ about going away.   happy

_ _ _ _ _ _ _ _ _ _ _

5. Dale will _____ the note to his pal.   write

_ _ _ _ _ _ _ _ _ _

6. It is _____ not to pay the store.   fair

_ _ _ _ _ _ _ _ _ _

7. Jack wants to _____ the grass.   plant

_____   _____

_ _ _ _ _ _ _ _   _ _ _ _ _ _ _ _

not cooked _____   spell again _____

_ _ _ _ _ _ _ _   _ _ _ _ _ _ _ _

not safe _____   use again _____

Directions: Add **dis** to each word, and use the new word to complete the sentence.

disobey
The prefix is **dis**.
The root word is **obey**.

1. One who steals is _____. honest

2. The lunchroom was in _____. order

3. It is wrong to _____ the law. obey

4. I _____ getting up in the morning. like

5. I _____ with what Ann said. agree

6. We had to _____ the wires. connect

7. The sun _____ my blue hat. colors

8. If you steal, people will _____ you. trust

LESSON 78: ADDING PREFIXES RE-; UN-; DIS-

Directions: At the top, add **un**, **dis**, or **re** to each root word to make a new word. At the bottom, add **un** or **dis** to each underlined word to change the meaning of the sentence. Print the word on the line.

un or **dis**

_____ please   _____ agree

_____ happy   _____ obey

_____ easy   _____ fair

re or **dis**

_____ color   _____ able

_____ write   _____ add

_____ send   _____ like

1. I wrapped my gift.

2. Sue obeyed Mother.

3. Pat will tie the bow.

4. He pleased Mother.

5. I agree with you.

6. It is safe to skate on the lake.

Directions: Choose the correct prefix to make sense in the sentence. Draw a ring around it.

1. Ann will __ check her paper.   re   dis

2. Jeff __ hooked the screen door for me.   un   dis

3. The books on the shelf are in __ order.   dis   re

4. Luke will __ wrap the package on the table.   dis   un

5. Did you __ read the story yet?   un   re

6. I __ like riding in trains.   re   dis

7. The ice is __ safe for skating.   un   re

8. Don't forget to __ pay the dime you owe Ed.   dis   re

9. The top of Jim's paper is __ even.   re   un

10. Jean __ liked the silly show.   re   dis

11. Father will __ screw this jar lid.   un   dis

12. I hurt my mother when I __ obey her.   dis   re

13. Carl and Mandy will __ plant the flowers.   un   re

14. Nancy is an __ selfish girl.   re   un

15. Will you please __ fold this paper?   re   dis

16. The thunder made us tremble and feel __ easy.   un   dis

Directions: At the top, find a word in the list that means almost the same as each word given. At the bottom, draw a ring around the word in each row that means almost the same as the first word.

Be a Good Thinker!

glad	car	fast
little	ill	large

big _____

happy _____

sick _____

small _____

auto _____

quick _____

1. **jolly**	sad	big	happy	jump
2. **clean**	slow	funny	unsoiled	big
3. **pile**	heap	near	rest	stop
4. **sleep**	awake	nap	paint	read
5. **hurt**	far	happy	sad	harm
6. **sick**	ill	quick	lazy	glad
7. **quick**	step	slow	pony	fast

Directions: Choose a word from the list at the top that means the opposite or almost the opposite of the word given, and print its numeral on the line.

1. old		8. wet		15. start	
2. full		9. slow		16. last	
3. down		10. hot		17. good	
4. short		11. out		18. well	
5. few		12. winter		19. long	
6. far		13. lower		20. shallow	
7. shut		14. awake		21. thick	

_____ dry		_____ up		_____ summer	
_____ short		_____ near		_____ fast	
_____ tall		_____ bad		_____ cold	
_____ thin		_____ sick		_____ many	
_____ stop		_____ upper		_____ first	
_____ deep		_____ new		_____ empty	
_____ open		_____ in		_____ asleep	

Directions: At the top, find the word that means almost the same as the given one and print its numeral on the line. At the bottom, print **S** if the two words mean almost the same. Print **O** if they mean almost opposite.

1. start	_____ big	1. cure	_____ sick
2. large	_____ unhappy	2. ill	_____ bigger
3. sad	_____ begin	3. larger	_____ close
4. glad	_____ stay	4. loud	_____ heal
5. quick	_____ happy	5. auto	_____ noisy
6. remain	_____ fast	6. shut	_____ car

first _____ last	stop _____ go	big _____ large
pail _____ bucket	quick _____ slow	happy _____ sad
choose _____ pick	tardy _____ late	bug _____ insect
little _____ small	top _____ bottom	float _____ sink
under _____ over	unhappy _____ sad	loud _____ noisy
hard _____ soft	bad _____ good	present _____ gift
creep _____ crawl	long _____ short	sweet _____ sour

Directions: In the first exercise, draw rings around the two words in each box having almost the same meaning. In the second exercise, draw rings around the two words in each box having almost opposite meanings.

unhappy	sad	big	green	brick	happy
door	barn	large	sky	just	glad

strike	hit	hair	stay	fast	fell
seed	shook	remain	home	quick	queen

three	tree	lift	raise	sick	snow
fat	chubby	drink	drop	ill	blow

bashful	fish	high	let	place	thin
shy	first	allow	top	slim	play

little	puppy	fly	fat	poor	candy
jelly	big	thin	penny	rich	good

they	fast	from	dirty	asleep	play
play	slow	clean	funny	baby	awake

take	turkey	out	in	door	chair
day	give	sleep	try	shut	open

bad	stood	wing	go	cold	fairy
come	good	come	wind	hot	spring

Directions: In the first exercise, find a word in the list at the top that sounds the same as the word given, and print it on the line. In the second, print the word to complete each sentence.

tail	here	to	meet	road	pail	heal	blue
week	cent	sail	maid	deer	pain	sea	

heel _____   see _____   rode _____

sent _____   tale _____   blew _____

weak _____   pale _____   hear _____

two _____   sale _____   made _____

meat _____   pane _____   dear _____

1. Can you _____ the bell ring loud and clear?   hear   here

2. Our puppy wagged its _____ when it saw us.   tale   tail

3. The _____ hid in the woods across the river.   deer   dear

4. We watched the _____ set in the west.   son   sun

Directions: In the first exercise, find a word in the list that sounds the same as the word given, and print it. In the second, choose a word from those above to complete each sentence.

son	meat	blew	to	pane	week
heel	here	beet	cent	sea	dear

hear _____

sent _____

deer _____

pain _____

sun _____

blue _____

two _____

see _____

weak _____

beat _____

heal _____

meet _____

1. I gave her _____ of my new books.

2. The _____ was shining in my window.

3. My pal _____ me a funny card.

4. The sky is very _____ today.

Directions: In the first exercise, draw a ring around the correct word, and print it on the line. Then in each box, find the word that sounds like the one given and print its numeral on the line.

1. Mother made me new _____ shorts.　　read　　red

2. Will you _____ me in school?　　meet　　meat

3. Your _____ hat is nice.　　blew　　blue

4. The store is having a _____ .　　sale　　sail

5. A ship is sailing on the _____ .　　see　　sea

6. Dad feels _____ today.　　weak　　week

1. sun ____ maid	1. tail ____ week	1. red ____ pair
2. seem ____ son	2. pale ____ pail	2. pear ____ read
3. made ____ seam	3. weak ____ tale	3. beat ____ beet
1. pane ____ pain	1. two ____ deer	1. ring ____ rode
2. in ____ blew	2. heel ____ too	2. road ____ here
3. blue ____ inn	3. dear ____ heal	3. hear ____ wring

Directions: Read the sentences at the top. Then answer the questions on the lines below.

1. Mother asked me to get sliced bread.
2. The flag hung on the big stage.
3. The stale candy bar was too hard to eat.
4. Mark burned his fingers on the hot corn.
5. Cathy got a purple coat for her birthday.
6. "Chirp! Chirp! Chirp!" sang the perky little bird.
7. Bruce put the mice in a huge cage.

1. What did Mother ask me to get? _____

2. Where did the flag hang? _____

3. What was too hard to eat? _____

4. On what did Mark burn his fingers? _____

5. What did Cathy get for her birthday? _____

6. Who sang "Chirp! Chirp! Chirp!"? _____

7. Where did Bruce put the mice? _____

Directions: Read the sentences at the top. Then answer the questions on the lines below.

1. The gardeners are filling two boxes with peaches.
2. The largest dog treated her puppies with kindness.
3. The cake-baking contest was conducted carelessly.
4. Jane sprinkled three spoonfuls of salt over the meat.
5. Stop saying, "I can't." Say, "I'll try!"
6. Mother doesn't know that the mail didn't come.
7. We've tried to study harder.

1. What are the gardeners filling with peaches?

2. How did the largest dog treat her puppies?

3. How was the cake-baking contest conducted?

4. How many spoonfuls of salt did Jane sprinkle?

5. What should you say?

6. What didn't come?

7. What have we tried to do?

Directions: Read the sentences at the top. Then answer the questions on the lines below.

1. Seth gave his uncle a new tie tack for his birthday.
2. Roy wrote an unfair report.
3. The crowds clapped as the silly clown bowed.
4. The witch with a crooked nose rode a broomstick.
5. "Shoo, Moo Cow!" cried the little boy.
6. Jean wore the leather belt with her sweater.
7. Paula had drawn the red shawl close to her.

1. What did Seth give to his uncle? _____

2. What did Roy write? _____

3. Who did the bowing? _____

4. What kind of a nose did the witch have? _____

5. What did the little boy cry to the cow? _____

6. What did Jean wear with her sweater? _____

7. What did Paula draw close to her? _____

DEFINITIONS AND RULES

The **vowels** are **a**, **i**, **u**, **o**, **e**, and sometimes **y** and **w**.

The **consonants** are the remaining letters and usually **y** and **w**.

A **consonant blend** consists of two or more consonants sounded together in such a way that each is heard—**black**, **train**, **cry**, **swim**, **spring**.

A **consonant digraph** consists of two consonants that together represent one sound—**when**, **thin**, **this**, **church**, **sheep**, **pack**, **know**, **write**.

A **vowel digraph** is a double vowel that does not follow Long-Vowel Rule I—**school**, **book**, **bread**, **auto**, **yawn**, **eight**.

A **diphthong** consists of two vowels blended together to form a compound speech sound—**cloud**, **boy**, **oil**, **cow**, **new**.

Short-Vowel Rule: If a word or syllable has only one vowel and it comes at the beginning or between two consonants, the vowel is usually short—**am**, **is**, **bag**, **fox**.

Long-Vowel Rule I: If a one-part word or syllable has two vowels, the first vowel is usually long and the second is silent—**rain**, **kite**, **cane**, **jeep**.

Long-Vowel Rule II: If a word or syllable has one vowel and it comes at the end of the word or syllable, the vowel is usually long—**we**, **go**, **cupid**, **pony**.

Y As a Vowel Rule:
   1) If **Y** is the only vowel at the end of a one-syllable word, **Y** has the sound of long **I**—**fly**, **try**, **by**.
   2) If **Y** is the only vowel at the end of a word of more than one syllable, **Y** has a sound almost like long **E**—**silly**, **funny**, **baby**.

Soft C and G Rule: When **c** or **g** is followed by **e**, **i**, or **y**, it is usually soft—**ice**, **city**, **change**, **gym**.